Second Labor

MOTHERS SHARE POST-BIRT[illegible]

Second Labor

Mothers Share Post-Birth Stories

EDITED BY

Chaya Kasse Valier

Set in ITC Legacy by Raphaël Freeman, Renana Typesetting
Cover design by Virtual Paintbrush
Cover painting: © agsandrew / Adobe Stock

ISBN: 978-0-9988551-0-3

To my supportive husband, Henry,
and our beloved children.

Contents

Foreword

Postpartum is a time of enormous change when virtually no aspect of a mother's life is unaffected. Postpartum mothers are at times full of awe and joy, and at other times with dread and utter panic, sometimes with very little in between. The mother is affected physically, cognitively, and emotionally, as follows:

- PHYSICALLY. The mother is no longer pregnant, and begins the process of healing from pregnancy and birth. Hormonally, her body undergoes massive shifts as it transitions from growing a baby internally to connecting with and feeding a baby.
- COGNITIVELY. Processing the birth, adjusting to the changed role as a mother, navigating the expanded family dynamics, a postpartum mother's mind is often racing. She is likely also overwhelmed with the details of caring for her new baby, whether it is her first child or she already has children.
- EMOTIONALLY. The mother is getting to know and love her baby, bonding as she holds him or her, while at the same time experiencing almost everything in technicolor intensity, thanks to the hormones, sleep deprivation, and long list of responsibilities. Some mothers are on pain medication or antidepressants that change the landscape of experiences. Isolation is also a very key factor.

Needless to say, postpartum is a time of adjustment like none other in life, and is a period during which mothers will certainly *feel.* With all the changes going on for the mother and the baby's entire family, it is little wonder that the postpartum period can be a challenging and intense time.

I encourage pregnant couples and new parents to be ready for anything, and to try to maintain a mindset of curiosity during difficult times if at all possible. This can help keep the logical thought process turned on when emotions are running away with us. I say this in one breath, and then with the next breath, I explain how this approach might be difficult to implement, given how hard it is to maintain perspective when you are exhausted and hormonally charged.

Over the years, I have searched for a book for postpartum mothers to really relate to, and haven't found one, until now. Bravo to Chaya Valier for compiling these beautiful and inspiring stories that are also very real. It is through this authentic sharing that the reader will know she is not alone, and can be inspired to likewise share her own experiences, both for herself and for others.

In the modern day, many new moms are not able to get the support they need, or feel ashamed to share their experiences or ask for help. This is where this book is so needed: In these pages, new mothers can feel connected, further understood and buttressed as they face the postpartum months ahead.

This book is also an excellent resource for fathers, other family members, and professionals to better understand the range of postpartum experiences. This book can have a global effect on addressing the need for successful support for postpartum mothers.

Warmly,
Alicia
Dr. Alicia H. Clark

Alicia H. Clark, PsyD, PLLC is a Licensed Clinical Psychologist in Washington, DC, and Assistant Professor at the Chicago School of Professional Psychology, Washington DC campus. Dr. Clark has been featured in TIME, Forbes, Huffington Post, Parents, Men's Health, SELF, *and other publications.*

Preface

The night after my fourth child was born, I was already hysterically crying from the baby's colic and my sleeplessness during the first twenty-four hours after giving birth. I was emotional not just from the initial shock of birth recovery coupled with baby care, but because I resentfully dreaded the upcoming few weeks or months of similar, seemingly unending struggles. As much as I felt blessed, awed, and elated each time we had a new baby, I was mired in the hardship of the "fourth trimester."

In the moment of that first night's emotional plight, I was inspired to compile a book of postpartum stories based on my own experiences and those of many other mothers I knew. As a mother and a doula, I witnessed that birth stories were freely shared, but after that people were quiet. As if they didn't know whether they were the only ones experiencing difficulty, or they were worried they weren't "doing it right," or they felt guilty. While Facebook and the like have opened up the channels of virtual group support, I wanted to compile a single book with shared stories from postpartum mothers.

I sensed that a compilation of personal stories would help mothers, birth professionals, mental health professionals, and fathers to have a book in hand to read about women's real postpartum experiences. The mothers can feel validated, knowing they're not alone, and even pleasantly, just sit back, relax, and vicariously experience other mothers' postpartum tales. In addition, the stories can spur on organizing support for postpartum mothers.

A midwife I know often quips, "We are pregnant for nine

months and postpartum for the rest of our lives." Jokes aside, the postpartum period is defined by professionals as any time up to two years after a birth. Generally speaking, though, people use the term *postpartum* for the first few months after having a baby. Yet this time period can indeed affect mothers, even in subtle ways, for the rest of their lives. No matter the definition, the time period after giving birth is like no other, and therefore mothers want to tell their post-birth stories, and read others.

While birth stories are welcome in our culture, post-birth stories are not given a forum. Birth stories are perceived as sexy, while the postpartum period is seen as anything but. Birth is finite, whereas postpartum goes on for a while, and therefore seemingly doesn't lend itself to the buildup-crescendo-conclusion of a story. Yet postpartum is full of stories, and this anthology seeks to fill our culture's postpartum story gap by giving voice to a wide spectrum of experiences. Some examples of topics include the breastfeeding-versus-formula quandary, not loving the baby until after a few months, razor-at-wrist postpartum depression, "rebirthing" a baby with Down syndrome, homebirths, C-sections, vaginal birth after cesarean (VBAC), a baby "so good you could have ordered her from a catalog," and many other enlightening and touching stories. Because each mother wrote so honestly, this anthology validates mothers and families, as well as provides detailed insights for anyone working with postpartum women.

There are plenty of books on the market about the postpartum period – most of them how-tos for baby's first year, or dedicated specifically to postpartum depression, or one person's autobiographical account of new motherhood. This anthology breaks from those three methods of postpartum discussion. Instead, by presenting multiple personal tales, this book fosters connection with all kinds of experiences, in turn raising grassroots awareness about the need for physical, emotional, and mental support for postpartum mothers.

All stories in this compilation of twenty-four autobiographical postpartum narratives are written by the contributing mothers. I specifically chose not to use the interview motif, opting instead to have each mother speak for herself via writing. Oftentimes, something deeper occurs when one writes rather than speaks.

People are experts in their own experiences. Motherhood is one special realm where this is always true, yet seldom acknowledged in the modern Western milieu. The contributors to this book are experts because, simply put, they are women who had new babies. These mothers wanted to write out their post-birth stories not only to share for themselves, but in order to possibly help others who might find themselves in similar postpartum situations. This book gave mothers the chance to express what it was really like for them postpartum, empowering and validating not only them, but all those who will read their stories.

Some contributors write professionally, most do not, and in order to preserve their true voices, edits were minimal. There is zero professional advice, yet a wealth of insights to be gleaned by laypeople and professionals alike.

Given that all of the writers come from modern, Western, English-speaking countries, I figured that out of the twenty-odd stories I was seeking, there would be a great deal of content overlap. Surprisingly, there were no redundancies - each story had a unique angle. All writers were given the same guidelines and the same questions as triggers. And yet, both organically and passionately, each took her own trajectory. Even though I did request some specific experiences - C-sections, homebirths, a mother whose last birth was at least fifteen years ago, a loss, a teen pregnancy, a grandmother, an adoption, etc. - nonetheless, the stories were often not what I expected.

These postpartum stories show struggle and strength, tribulations and growth, sadness and coping, pain and recovery, shock, wonderment, and joy. All of the stories brought me to tears at least once, and many made me laugh out loud.

And there's even more. As the mothers submitted their stories, I was struck by what turned out to be the other side of the coin:

the process of writing helped the writers themselves. *Cathartic* was an oft-used word to describe the opportunity for giving voice to their postpartum experiences. I hope that reading a book of post-birth stories will open a gateway for other mothers to also write or otherwise tell their own stories.

To Abbie, Abby, Aimee, Amanda, Andrea, Beth, Caitlin, Carmiya, Carol, Elisheba, Hannah, Hilary, Jen, Jill, Kathy, Leah, Miriam C., Miriam G., Natalie, Rachel, Renanit, Sarah, and Tali – thank you so very much for your powerful, moving, and inspirational sharing.

In support,
Chaya

Acknowledgments

Apropos to the stories in this book, they say that writing a book is like giving birth. Having been through both processes, I can attest that it's true. Little did I know that compiling, editing, writing, proofreading, proofreading, proofreading, and proofreading again, working with the graphic designer for the front and back covers, typesetting and finally publishing this book would equate to a pregnancy, birth, and postpartum period in its own right.

When deciding to collect these stories, I knew I was taking on a part-time job, but I wanted it – this literal labor of love. People ask me how I did it, what with being a working mother of five children ages 12 and younger, and the answer is: piecemeal. As I write this acknowledgment, I'm procrastinating tax filing, writing assignments for clients, and readying the requisite snacks for after-preschool pickup. Every once in a while, I would simply put other priorities on hold and tackle the next stage of this book.

A running theme throughout the mothers' stories in this book is the need for support. Likewise, as with any pregnancy, birth and postpartum period, I was able to take on this project largely due to a strong network of encouragement and professional advice. I am grateful for the backing I received from people who wanted this type of book on their shelves, and hadn't yet come across it. As one example, psychologist Dr. Alicia Clark, for whom I worked as a writing assistant, swiftly accepted when I asked her whether she would be interested in writing this book's foreword.

I would also like to specifically thank the other professionals who took part in the publishing process: Laura Mazer, Executive Editor of Seal Press for her consultation (and friend and literary extraordinaire Dan Schifrin for putting us in touch); editorial consultant Charlotte Friedland for structural ideas; book shepherd and publicist Stuart Schnee for being my go-to with the entire process, including suggesting a superb editor, Kezia Raffel Pride, graphic designer Shanie Cooper, and typesetter Raphaël Freeman. I also extend warm thank-yous to proofreaders Jenna Rose Alpern, Netanya Carmi, Andrea Krissman Deitch, Batsheva Goldstein, Abby Hazony, Eryca Kasse, Renanit Levy, Yael Valier, and Carmiya Weinraub.

Other family members and friends peppered this book with their ideas, and many of the writers offered suggestions, too. In particular, I'm grateful to my husband, Henry, who is proud of me pursuing this project, and didn't question the involvement necessary to make it happen.

I am honored to have all of your support.

The births in these stories took place between 1998 and 2013, with the exception of the story "Still Today." The majority of the stories occurred between 2008 and 2013.

~ ~ ~

Identifying details have been altered in some stories.

First Baby:
Why Didn't Anyone Warn Me?

Getting It

I was extremely nervous about actually having a baby. Not the labor part, but the having-of-the-baby part. The living-with-a-baby part.

CARMIYA W.
MOTHER, MASTERS IN SOCIAL WORK
AGE 33
FIRST OF THREE BIRTHS

I know myself very well. So when mothers asked me, in my thirty-ninth and fortieth weeks of pregnancy, if I wasn't just ready to have this baby already, I answered, "No, I could wait longer," because I was extremely nervous about actually having a baby. Not the labor part, but the having-of-the-baby part. The living-with-a-baby part. The not-going-back-to-just-my-husband-and-me-only part. I was also pretty certain that labor would be boring. Many mothers thought I was strange when I commented that that was what I was expecting.

I was right – for me, the actual labor part was BORING. There was so much time from the first contraction until active labor that I got bored just waiting for the next contraction to come, for the next thing to happen. (When can we go to the hospital, already? When can we call the doula? When can we talk to the doctor? When will the nurse come back in?) Really, for all my births, the waiting for things to really get going part is super boring for me.

But then we actually had the baby. A girl. Which we found funny. We had expected a boy based on all of the (incorrect) guesses people had wagered. So when the doctor said, "It's a girl," my husband and I both laughed.

Nursing was not easy at first. Not a problem with production, but mostly a problem with latching and baby sleepiness. I think it was day 5, and my mom told me we had to get out a bit for some fresh air. I believe she quoted her mother, my grandmother Eva, of blessed memory, in saying: "Nothing happens if you don't go anywhere," so we left the apartment and walked around. We ran into a mother from the neighborhood who wanted to meet the bundle in my carrier. After oohing and aahing (and me thinking, "Doesn't anybody remember how hard this is?!"), she inquired, "Are you nursing?" I said, "Yes," and thought, "You nosy woman," and she said, "Oh, I miss it! We just weaned. My daughter is fourteen months. You're so lucky."

This comment, though well intended, made me feel lonely, because I couldn't connect to someone who had enjoyed nursing. I knew I wanted to do it, but it felt like a JOB, a job I didn't like but had to do, not a joy or a gift or a blessed peaceful moment of zen of whatever maternal-baby connection one is "supposed" to feel.

Given how difficult it was to wake my baby, but that she had no trouble gaining weight, by day 6 I decided to stop following the hospital advice of feeding every three hours and to just watch her hunger signs. After twenty-four hours, she had eaten ten times, so I was satisfied that I could trust her to tell me when she was hungry. This was the start of a really strong belief in on-demand feeding as being best for my babies, but also a pull and tug in my heart about this being the hardest way to mother.

On-demand feeding worked great for me with baby attachment, for trusting in baby, and for learning about baby's needs. But on-demand feeding made me feel powerless. And annoyed. And angry. Especially from 7 to 11 P.M., when her on-demand feedings were constant. After 11 P.M., she would sleep for four hours, sure, but from week 1 to week 7, that 7 to 11 P.M. time slot was a huge hindrance in my life. I read some, I watched some TV, I talked on the phone, but I was stuck, never knowing when she'd need to nurse again. I was annoyed about being stuck. And angry about being stuck.

Some women have postpartum depression, and that must be really hard. I say I had postpartum annoyance. I didn't like changing diapers. I didn't like feeding on demand (but I was proud of it). I didn't like changing her clothes. I didn't like giving her a bath. I didn't like missing out on social events and saying my morning prayers. And I especially did NOT like wondering, "When will she wake up?" More than anything, that aspect of parenting has been hard - the hardest thing is not being in control of knowing when the baby will wake up or go to sleep. Which really means not knowing how much, or when, I will have time to myself.

Sometime before five weeks, I was walking around the neighborhood with my husband, and a woman greeted us, again with this scenario of oohing and aahing over the baby. This happened a lot, and on the one hand I liked the attention, but on the other hand, it continued to make me feel lonelier, as it had on day 5. Because the ooh-ers and aah-ers said things like: "How cute," "Congratulations," "Enjoy her," and "I remember those days..." These people conveyed that this was a precious time, a sweet time, a time to be joyful and appreciate. But I didn't feel any of those things.

I wanted to scream at these people, "Don't you remember how terrible this part is? All the diaper changes, all the laundry, all the crying, all the demands, all the lost moments of independence, all the separation from everything you used to be able to do so easily?!" After a particular woman oohed and aahed, I said to my husband, "Doesn't anyone remember how hard this is?" and he said, "Maybe she didn't think it was hard." This made me feel even worse.

The first three months, I felt very distant from my husband.

I didn't think he "got it" – which was mostly the nursing part, the taking-her-everywhere part, the being on demand all day and night part. When I went back to work part-time, he watched her during the day, and then he definitely got it. I felt more connected to him at that point, and I felt more connected to our daughter, too, because I got a chance to miss her.

I really started enjoying her at five months. That's when I actually thought, "Oh… this is what people mean when they say it's fun." She was laughing then, and interacting, and playing, and becoming a person. I started to love her then, too.

Walking the Talk

Generally, I like new things. But this. This was something different. Overwhelming. Disconcerting. Unsettling. Ostracizing.

HILARY F.
MARKETING, CONTENT CREATION, AND SOCIAL MEDIA
AGE 38 (31 AT THE TIME OF THE BIRTH)
FIRST OF THREE BIRTHS

I had a very corporate job, a very corporate wardrobe, and a very corporate life. I was more comfortable in any one of my sixteen dry-cleaned, well-pressed black suits than I was in sweats. I worked sixty-hour weeks and flew around the country, delivering lectures and firing people. They paid me well.

Then we decided to move cities and have kids. New location. New apartment. New life. New baby.

Generally, I like new things. Shiny new shoes sitting neatly in their boxes. A new kitchen gadget guaranteed to halve my prep time. Soft, new embroidered bath towels with my initials, from a catalog.

But this. This was something different. Overwhelming. Disconcerting. Unsettling. Ostracizing.

I had a birth plan, like any good Midwestern American overachiever. People told me all my life, "Them's birthin' hips." They weren't. My body failed me, and I failed in the birth. After the emergency cesarean, complete with rushing and stretcher and blinking lights and raised voices, everyone vanished. My husband. The baby. The team of doctors and anesthesiologists and stitcher-uppers. They abandoned me in a hallway, on a rolling bed, until I was assigned a room. It could have been ten minutes or three hours; I'll never know.

My husband eventually returned, and the nurses told him that since it was the middle of the night, he should go home to sleep and I should wait patiently until the 5 A.M. feeding, at which time they'd bring me the baby. Not before then.

It was 11 P.M.

I spent that night in tears. Alone. That was the first night of many like it.

Every staff member who came near me that night – to check blood pressure, to administer Tylenol (which is all they allow after they cut your abdominal muscles in half) – was greeted with choked-up begging. Why can't I have my baby? Where is she? Here I was, all tear-stained, hormonal, and colostrum-leaky. I don't remember their precise answers, just that they weren't bringing me my baby yet.

Finally, around 5 A.M., they brought me my baby as promised. They wheeled her – in a little portable cart bassinet – next to my bed. Then they departed. Little did I know that immediately after a cesarean, you can barely sit up unassisted, let alone get out of bed, pick your baby up out of a bassinet, climb back into bed, and situate yourself to nurse.

I cried some more.

My husband, who had little more clue than I did about babies, had switched jobs the week I gave birth. He had been commuting ninety minutes each direction to a high-tech job, and was successful, just the week before, in securing employment closer to home. The first week on a new job is not the time to ask for personal days, new baby or not. So he showed up as much as he could and helped as much as he could, but that wasn't very much.

I was hungry. Every day around the noon hour, an announcement came over the PA system with a muffled voice. Meanwhile, I kept waiting for someone to bring me a meal.

No one did.

It turns out, I discovered after day 3, that postpartum mothers are expected to travel down the hall to the cafeteria, where meals are served. I had no idea – it simply didn't occur to me, in my post-surgery haze, to ask. Visitors had been bringing snacks, and the nurse said, very sternly, that I wasn't allowed solid food before I pooped. So in bed I stayed. Attempting to muster a poop.

Nursing wasn't going well, yet I was determined. Again with the Midwestern work ethic. The first nurse on duty showed me how to feed the baby on one side and instructed me to wait until the next feeding to offer her the other side. The next nurse on duty differed from the first, and told me to empty both breasts at each feeding. Conflicting instructions when you've just given birth are difficult to bear. I kept nursing, the baby kept screaming, and I had so much milk that I was both leaking and in pain.

Day 5, and they tell me I can go home the following morning. I hadn't even realized so much time had passed. My husband pointed out the window and tried to comfort me by saying that the next time the sun came up, I could go home. I had not realized there was a window in my room. I had retreated so far internally in an (unsuccessful) effort to handle it all that my entire universe had been reduced to a tiny three-meter "cell" which housed my bed and a chair. He did his best to transmit all the discharge instructions, including the fact that there was a lactation consultant on duty and available for consultation two hours each morning, for free. Considering that the nursing was getting worse – not better – I decided to make the difficult journey down the hall to her office. She wouldn't come to me just as the food wouldn't. No one comes to you here.

She watched as I tried to nurse our baby, while I winced and cried as my frustrated, hungry daughter cried too. She diagnosed us in three seconds flat – our baby was "tongue tied." She couldn't stick her tongue out far enough to latch properly. She had been getting nothing but drops of milk from me since she was born. My baby was starving. Now I had not only failed at birth, I had failed at mothering.

The surgeon was called. I was released from the hospital, so I had nowhere I was allowed to be. We waited outside the surgery room while he clipped the connective tissue under her tongue. When I heard her scream, I cried even more.

But after the clipping, she instantly nursed like a champ. And wanted food. Every twenty minutes. All day long.

Baby and I went home - and my husband, to work. There I was, with a sparkly stroller and a Baby Bjorn - and no clue. I did the only thing I have ever known how to do when faced with an overwhelming situation. I self-educated. I took control. I read *Secrets of the Baby Whisperer* and almost memorized it. I charted the nursing: which side, how many minutes and seconds, how many dirty diapers she produced, and when. I documented it all. My nonjudgmental husband tried to go along with this new chart-heavy regimen without questioning it. He sensed that I had slipped into near-panic and both of us were helpless. The *Baby Whisperer* (my new bible) warned against nursing more often than every two hours. The baby did not require it, she said.

So I didn't.

I held and walked and bounced my screaming, crying, desperate baby all day, every day, but refused to nurse her more often than every two hours.

My grip on reality, along with the mounting sleep deprivation, became more severe. I spent zero time away from the baby. We had no structure to our days, no mother popping by to grant me a nap or a shower, and no idea that Crazed Overwhelm was the battle cry of most new mothers.

I found solace in walking. Once my scar was healed more or less, and I could be up and around more, I took to taking long walks. There I was, a young mother pushing her beautiful sleeping baby in a high-end stroller. Life MUST be good. It LOOKED good. So it MUST BE good.

Since the only time the baby ceased screaming was either during nursing time or during walk time, that's all we did. I walked four, six, sometimes eight hours each day. Delirious with overwhelming emotions that no one else seemed to identify with (and I was too ashamed to voice publicly), I walked and walked. People told me I looked incredible (walking most of your waking hours does take that baby weight off). I walked from my neighborhood to the center of the city and back again. From insular neighborhoods to industrial neighborhoods, to the mall and back. I walked from one park to another. I walked to the post office on the other side of town, just to buy stamps.

I had no particular purpose to my days, and was losing what self-respect I had worked so hard in corporate America to earn. I documented exactly WHAT was so difficult each month, so as to remind myself if I ever thought about having another baby - not to. I still have those records.

A Dose of Humor, A Dose More of Knowledge

I had learnt about postpartum depression and possible signs to look out for during my college and training. But it seems as though they forgot to mention the other stuff that happens.

HANNAH G.
TEACHER AND MOM
AGE 30
FIRST BIRTH

Throughout pregnancy, I knew I wanted to have a natural birth. Growing up, I had personally tried never to take medication unless absolutely necessary. I had trained as a nurse in birth and childcare, so I was aware generally of all the options available within the British hospitals, and I had decided it was vital that I find out what the policies of our local hospital were, specifically with regard to natural birthing.

I read books, spoke to people online, spoke to friends who had already experienced birth, and spoke to my teachers who had given birth multiple times to try to find out what birth was like.

After finding out more information, I decided to go ahead with my natural birth. During triage, when the nurse-midwife asked me if I wanted an epidural, I said, "No, thank you." She had a look of shock on her face – it was the look a parent would give a child who had refused chocolate in the candy shop. As the contractions became more intense, I kept thinking that I had to be close to the end, but no, this baby was happy taking his time. I was asked multiple times again about epidural and other pain relief. I had now been in labor almost eighteen hours.

When I thought the contractions were at their peak, I was told I was 10 cm dilated. Well, I was exhausted, I was on the bed and I was getting delirious, and all I kept saying was, "Can I just go to sleep?" Well, this caused my doula and husband to start rolling about laughing – I was so glad they were entertained!

Finally, my midwife came in. All I saw were her rubber gloves, and she said this is it, final stage. She told my doula to call her when I was ready to push, but before she could leave the room, I was ready. The midwife was incredible, and as they were shocked that throughout labor I had wanted nothing for the pain, I had some more nurses and midwives in the room watching, my midwife shouting, "Fabulous! Fabulous!" They are not used to natural births for first-timers – most need coaching to push since they're on epidurals.

Thank God, my baby boy was born happy and healthy. The overall experience of a natural birth was incredible; I was blessed to be able to achieve it. I did have complications, though. I had torn as many women do. However, even after they stitched up the tears, they realized the ice water poured over me to clean the area could not do much – I was still bleeding. No matter how hard they tried, they couldn't find the cause, so they were concerned I was hemorrhaging. Therefore, they took me to surgery to see what was going on. My baby was given to my husband before being taken to the nursery.

They gave me an epidural so they could check internally and externally and do whatever was necessary. They had to do additional stitches in various places to stop the bleeding, but thank God it was multiple tears, not hemorrhaging. They then had to give me two bags of blood, which I never knew could make me so happy.

Looking back, the highlight of the birth was the fact that I had a natural delivery with humor in the room throughout birth. I was a little scared about what was happening to me after the epidural during surgery – I had no feeling in my legs, I was thirsty but was not allowed to drink, I was exhausted, nauseated, and all I wanted was to hold my baby. My firstborn son – and I was not able to be with him to breastfeed him. So without recourse, I was taken to the ward, and as any British person would say, I had a nice cup of tea.

Eventually my son was brought to me. I truly wished people had told me that I was going to have to be completely off my feet! I was devastated, I couldn't even move while the epidural was still in my system, I had postpartum bleeding, and I was feeling sorry for myself. I couldn't understand all the instructions thrown at me by the doctors, but then the nurses were great – they explained everything to me. They carried my son to the bed, as I couldn't get him out of his bassinet. I was even too weak to breastfeed at this stage.

Finally, after two blood transfusions and three days of plenty of TLC in the hospital, my baby boy and I were sent home. I was under strict instructions to rest. Well, that's easier said than done. Day 4 postpartum I was home, both sets of parents were here, and I was exhausted, I just wanted rest, yet I felt if I attended to myself, I would be depriving my son. Breastfeeding was still not happening, and I was feeling down and very emotional. My brother, a father of two, also came in from out of town. I had decided to take him up on the offer of rest, so he looked after the baby.

A week later, I was still weak, I was bleeding, the stitches were painful, my body ached, I couldn't stand for long, and I was still continually exhausted. I thought of all those women I had seen a week after they had a baby, and their figures looked great – they looked so healthy and glowing. And I looked like a ghost. I had learnt about postpartum depression and possible signs to look out for during my college and training. But it seems as though they forgot to mention the other stuff that happens.

The bleeding that can go on for weeks. The return of your period and how it won't be like you used to have it. They say sometimes you have unwanted guests after giving birth - well, my period was one of them!

After a few days, all my family had gone back to their homes, and I was left to fend for myself during the day, so I stayed on the sofa and cuddled my bundle of joy. I was still feeling weak - the pain of the stitches was starting to ease off, but at least I was able to get up by myself to get a cup of water. Still no breastfeeding, and that was heartbreaking for me. I had tried pumps and lactation consultants, and still nothing. As each day passed, though, I started feeling stronger and stronger.

One incident in particular that made me feel stronger was when I watched my husband hold our son. I was the channel in bringing our beautiful child into the world. Seeing my son look at me the way he did made my heart melt - I knew that no matter how weak I might have felt, my husband and son were giving me strength. I thought back to the birth - I was so grateful for my doula, but more than anything, I could not have done any of it without my husband.

By six weeks I felt a little more normal. I still had to be careful physically, but was feeling a bit happier emotionally, in myself. I had started breastfeeding along with giving formula, and although I was still not producing enough milk, at least I was achieving something. I had to see my ob-gyn, as my bleeding went on for ten weeks, followed by a two-week menstrual period.

After almost five months, my body is now getting back on track. I took my son for his checkup at the Baby Wellness Center, and the nurse did a postpartum questionnaire to see if I was depressed. I was OK. I had made sure to let out my emotions the whole time. I never held back. I got asked by friends if I would have pain relief for the next birth - I said no. I was thrilled I got to fully experience this birth. Although I had a long journey of healing, I know that I would do it all again the same way.

Even though I'd studied birth and childcare myself, it was lost on me until it was me in those shoes. I just would have preferred to have learnt and been prepared for the postpartum period not years beforehand during my studies, but rather in the last weeks of my first pregnancy. Maybe that would have helped.

Advice

Many mothers, grandmothers, and random strangers didn't hesitate to ask me that one glaring question: Is your baby sleeping through the night?

Chaya V.
Wife and mother, doula, content writer, masseuse
Age 40 (33 at the time of the birth)
First of four births

After we had our first child, I was convinced that the new-baby care thing was part of a conspiracy. That is to say, during your pregnancy, all other parents had decided NOT to tell you about what it's really like once you have a baby. Like they shy away from the truth, not wanting to scare you about the daunting scenario that's in store for you for the first few weeks, if not months, of a new baby.

To be sure, I'd been warned with the following phrase: "Better do *x* [travel abroad, go out for dinner, go dress shopping, SLEEP] NOW because once you have a BABY..."

I'd also heard about colic, about parents pacing back and forth with a newborn, about the ten to twelve diapers a day (although – full disclosure – I never ended up changing more than six times a day), and about how much laundry new babies generate. I even attended a La Leche League meeting BEFORE I had the baby, where the leader explained: "You might be nursing every one and a half hours, *FOR AN HOUR*. So what are you going to do during that half an hour? Take a shower? Put in a load of laundry? Make yourself a sandwich (to eat *while breastfeeding*)?"

But still, these were just words, ideas, pies in the sky. As if they would not apply to me. I would, of course, just be able to calm the baby down with soothing massages and the right aura.

The point is: nothing could have prepared me for an actual newborn. As I have heard so many new mothers say, over and over again, *I couldn't get past the birth.* I spent most of my first pregnancy reading all about pregnancy, and all about birth. The new baby – the real, live little human who would emerge from me into my and my husband's arms – remained theoretical.

Once I was faced with a baby who was screaming her head off, after I'd nursed her incessantly, gotten her to burp and poop (changed her twice), and cooled her down with water, I was at a loss. I had no idea what to do. It was, simply put, awful. Why, if I put her down when she was asleep after nursing, would she wake up ten minutes later? Why, if I took her out of the sling, would she wake up? What happened to the "sleeps like a baby" idea? During the night, she would sleep and nurse in between, but the days had no breaks – she would fuss whenever I put her down. Weren't babies supposed to nap?

Only with later babies did I realize this meant she was "off," resulting in her being overtired, that I'd needed to get the baby on a routine and not just rely on the baby carrier to get her to sleep during the day. This went on for eight or nine months with our first two children, and I was like, "Check me in to the loony bin, now, please." Only when they got on a daytime napping routine did things become manageable. I'd read stuff online from day 1, but I mostly found "sleep training" didn't seem to jive with daytime naps. Thankfully (as if miraculously) I later found two books that people had recommended, and their systems worked.

With my third and fourth children, I implemented the napping routine as soon as possible – most books, and parents, say around seven weeks it can kick in, and seven weeks is a TON different from eight or nine months!

With our first baby, I was annoyed, disappointed, and confused as to why, when I complained to other mothers about the short naps during the day, NO ONE asked me, "What's your baby's routine?" or "Is your baby on a routine?" I think these seasoned mothers were so conditioned to staying away from giving advice that they didn't even know how to ask a question in a way that wouldn't sound like advice. So they just didn't ask.

The way I saw it, though, I needed help, and no one gave it to me. Or perhaps these women never had my problem. Or perhaps no one heard my desperation – perhaps I was just commiserating on the playground bench. Small talk, as it were.

Now, while on the one hand people shied away from giving me advice, on the other hand many mothers, grandmothers, and random strangers didn't hesitate to ask me that one glaring question: *Is your baby sleeping through the night?*

Here again, I learned several lessons from this question. Firstly, what does "sleeping through the night" mean? Does it mean twelve hours? Five hours? Many "experts" say it's five hours – as if five hours is THROUGH THE NIGHT? With nursing/bottle, or without? What?

Do YOU, as an adult, sleep through the night, or do you get up to pee? If you get up to pee, does that ruin your own adult "through the night" definition?

I learned to be very discerning when mothers would speak about how and when their babies slept "through the night." One mother of a one-year-old told me her baby slept through the night at six weeks. After careful questioning, I realized she meant from 1 A.M. to 5 A.M.!

Generally speaking, there's sleeping through the night with feeds and without. With feeds means the baby eats, then goes right back to sleep. None of this walking/rocking/shushing for hours on end. With our babies, this happened after around four to six weeks. But no wakeups at all, not even to feed? Certainly they couldn't mean THAT for a two-month-old, right?

The bottom line is I learned to ask what the definitions are, and to feel comfortable with my current situation if it's working fine for both baby and me. If not, we can work to change it.

These questions and discussions made me more deeply aware – when speaking with other mothers on the playground bench – that they might be in desperation regarding the child issue they're conversing about with me. I've learned to listen, and also to ask, "What's your instinct?" and "What do you feel would be the easiest for you and your baby?" and to let them talk it out for themselves first. We mothers are really strong in our instincts about our children, and we can usually use our guts and our hearts to arrive at our own solutions.

But instincts often need tools to carry out solutions, and I, like most modern Western mothers, didn't grow up knowing about the tools, so I needed to learn them. Glued to Google, I read, and read, and read. Tools included baby books that spoke to us, parenting courses, a different bottle nipple type, just the right jogger stroller to get some exercise while baby sleeps or happily gazes around (hopefully), prayer, or figuring out how to get my spa-at-home (aka a twenty-minute shower when no one else is in the house – sheer luxury!).

I'm writing this as our fourth child, eight weeks old, is napping soundly in her stroller, swaddled tight, with the pacifier. This, after she nursed, had "activity wakeful period," and then started to whimper. That meant she's ready to sleep. I tried for an inordinately long time – seven weeks – without that passy. I didn't want to have to wean her from it when she's two years old, only to have her replace it with her thumb like with my second child. But in the end, that's what consoles her during the day, so I went for it. Now we have a life – she gets sleep, and I get a break. We're both happiest this way, and the passy weaning thing will just have to play itself out. All in a day of new mothering.

Take It Easy

The scene in the dining hall was a metaphor: Trying to figure out how to juggle our food trays with our baby carts reflected our need to manage our babies' needs with our own.

MIRIAM C.
FUNDRAISER
AGE 30
FIRST OF TWO BIRTHS

The birth itself was fairly uneventful. I got to the hospital dilated at 3.5 cm. The contractions were bearable but I figured, why suffer? Had an epidural. Not the best move, since it immobilized me and slowed things down. But it did mean I could sleep. I slept through the entire labor and only woke up when the midwife turned off the epidural so that I would start pushing. My husband jokes that he was very disappointed in my pregnancy and delivery: I had no crazy cravings and did not send him out on midnight runs for pickles and ice cream. I did not scream or curse in labor; the worst thing I said was, "It freaking hurts."

It was a totally positive experience, and the best part was the complete sense of trust that I had in my husband and the team of midwives who birthed me. Like I said, the only negative was that I took the epidural too early and was immobilized for the rest of labor, which meant I lost a bit of the control that I wanted to have in the process.

Being the crazy planner and active doer that I am, as soon

as they wheeled me out of delivery and into a room, I went into "planning" mode. It seemed everything needed organizing. My husband kept reminding me to slow down, but I was too excited. Nursing went well from the very start, and we were all feeling good. The pain from the stiches and hemorrhoids was pretty intense, but the nurses encouraged me to take over-the-counter painkillers and gave me those wonder-gel sanitary pads that made things much better.

I got dressed in real clothes each and every day. I did not feel sick or tired, and knew that if I stayed in my pajamas I would get lazy. That being said, I was surprised when the nurse told me that meals were served in the communal dining room at the end of the hall. I was thinking, "I just pushed a human out of my body. The least you could do is bring me my food."

Thankfully, visitors brought me lots of goodies which kept me well fed for the first day and night. But by breakfast the next morning (served in the hospital at 6:30 A.M. after they bring you your baby from the nursery at 6 A.M. – how is anyone supposed to sleep and recuperate when keeping these kinds of hours?!), I had to get something to eat.

I wheeled my little guy's bassinet bed down the hall, and as I was waddling my way there, I understood this scenario as part of the healing process. Seeing all these women who just went through the same thing made me realize that my postpartum waddle was normal. The scene in the dining hall was like a metaphor for what we were all feeling: trying to figure out how to juggle our food trays with our baby carts reflected our need to manage our babies' needs with our own. Deciding how to sit without wincing in pain yielded recognition that every part of our being, every basic step we take in life from here on out, would be influenced by the birth of these magnificent creatures. Maneuvering the baby bassinet carts so they would not be in the way of other mamas was good training for the stroller-Tetris that always seems to be in play at supermarkets, at the mall, on the playground, and when crossing the street.

When it was time to leave the hospital (day 3 after birth), I was ready. When we got home, my mother had lunch prepared and all the baby clothes were washed and folded. My only job was to rest. I took a brief nap and then felt like I was going stir-crazy. I strapped little man into his new stroller and we went out for a walk. Everyone thought I was nuts, but I felt good about being so up and about. If it feels good to you, it can't be bad, right? Well, wrong. But keep reading.

Even while I was nursing the baby (every two hours), my brain was in overdrive about the things that needed to get done. Who I could delegate them to, what I would do myself, and when everything could/would be complete.

At our first pediatrician visit (day 5), she was concerned about the baby's color and sent us back to the hospital's nursery for repeat bilirubin tests. This really threw me off my game. Here I was thinking I had it all together. My husband and I were doing great, baby was eating/sleeping/pooping. What could the hospital do for him that we were not already doing?! The testing itself was pretty easy; waiting for the results was annoying. But while we were hanging around in the nursery, I got my first taste of mama guilt.

All the postpartum nurses and mothers were chatting with us and asking us how old our little guy was. When I said that he was five days old, they all looked at me and said, "What? And you're walking around? You need to rest." One old-timer nurse even said, "You shouldn't even be taking the baby out for the first thirty days of his life!" All of a sudden a wave of "I am a bad mother" hit me. I kept thinking that I was not normal or a fit parent because I was feeling so good and strong. Because my baby and I were not struggling with the nursing, I was clearly doing something wrong. The fact that he was a good sleeper and that I was not sleeping when he was sleeping meant that there was something amiss with us both.

It took my husband a good few hours to calm me down. He kept reminding me that everyone figures the motherhood thing out at their own pace. And that even though we were first-time parents, we had found our rhythm quickly.

By a week after the birth, my physical strength had returned and the pain had subsided. I felt so blessed to be surrounded by my visiting family and friends, and realized that each and every one of those people had a part to play in my baby's life. But a lot of them said some variation of "Please sit down, you should not be running around like this." Remembering how I felt after our return trip to the nursery, I politely responded with, "Thank you for your concern. I'm feeling great."

I was also having so much fun snacking on all the leftovers from meals people brought us, and opening all their gifts. I made piles of things to return to various stores, and my mom and I planned to hit the mall the very next day. We all had a good night's sleep, and I did feel good, so on day 9, we headed out to do some returning and shopping.

But halfway through our excursion, I started to feel sick. I had hot flashes while I was nursing the baby. A few mothers who were also in the nursing room asked me if I was feeling OK because my color changed from pink to white to green. I felt like I had been hit by a ton of bricks. Everything ached. I was shivering and I could barely hold the baby because my hands were so numb. My mother whisked us all home and made me get into bed. She checked my temperature (I did have a fever), had me check my bleeding, and made sure that I stayed hydrated.

I did not know this at the time, but when my husband came home from work, my mother suggested that he take me back to the hospital because she was concerned that I had some kind of postpartum infection. They decided to wait it out until the next day. If I was still unwell by morning, he would take me in. Each time the baby had to nurse, my husband would prop him up on a pillow next to me, help him latch on, wait ten minutes and then change sides. I was too weak to do any of this. Another dose of mother guilt set in: What kind of mother cannot hold her own baby? What kind of mother gets so sick that she can't be left alone with her little one?

By the next morning I was feeling better. I spoke to my doctor, who recommended that I take it easy and that I call him if my fever came back. He was convinced that I had just done too much too soon. He reminded me that I had delivered a baby only nine days prior, and that there was a reason women are supposed to rest after birth.

I tried my best to take this advice to heart. I began letting people do more things for us, and I handed over the organizational tasks to my mother and mother-in-law. I still went out for walks, but they were shorter. I still made sure we had a hot dinner every day, but did not feel guilty when it was a meal that someone else had brought over as opposed to one I had made myself. I learned to accept that I did not have to do it all alone. The fact that my baby was relatively calm and easy did not mean I didn't have to take it easy myself.

From the very outset, my husband and I decided that we wanted our baby to have good and healthy habits, particularly about sleep. It was very important to us that he learn to fall asleep on his own, that he not need us to rock/sway/hold him, and that he have a semi-schedule. We worked hard at this and had it down by three weeks. While we did these things for the baby, I knew that they were going to make life easier for us too. We knew what to expect when. We could anticipate his needs and plan accordingly. The established routine made sure we all had our day more-or-less planned; fewer unknowns made it easier to deal with any surprises that might have popped up. Knowing more or less why he was crying reduced my stress levels. The other thing that we pushed for was a pacifier. We bought three kinds and let baby decide which he liked. The fact that he took a pacifier from a young age made it easier to keep to a schedule. If he cried between meals and he wasn't dirty, the pacifier kept him calm.

At one month, I joined a baby massage course so that I could meet other mothers and learn new ways to interact with the baby. I met up with friends and made sure to have at least one hour of serious adult non-baby-related conversation a day. My husband, parents, in-laws, and friends helped make sure I found the right balance between keeping busy and taking it easy. Everyone pitched in by doing laundry, making meals, keeping me company, and doing grocery runs.

I think the two most significant lessons for me from my first birth experience were: (1) I can wait it out with the epidural, so that I can be more mobile during labor, and (2) taking it easy is OK – even if I feel good, I have to remember that my body is healing and that more than anything, my baby needs a strong and sane mother.

I took both of these lessons to heart when it came time to birth number two, and I pray that I will remember them in the future as well.

On a Plane at Three Weeks

The nurse at the Baby Wellness Clinic encouraged me to go to my family in South Africa where I had a support system. In the third week of my child's life, I took her on a plane, by myself, to a different continent.

TALI G.
NONPROFIT PROFESSIONAL,
CURRENTLY STAY-AT-HOME MOM AND PART-TIME TEACHER
AGE 29
FIRST BIRTH

I have always liked to feel in control of almost every aspect of my life, and my birth was no different. I read a ton of material and attended birthing classes before the big day arrived.

Of course, nothing worked out the way I had imagined. I underestimated the pain of contractions, convincing myself that I am stronger than most people and would be fine, but after a thirty-nine-hour labor, which included being sent home from the hospital, membrane stripping, an epidural, and having my waters broken, I now know that giving birth is one of those times in your life when the only choice is to hand yourself over to a Higher Being and let go.

I wish my story were less bleak. I feel guilty sharing it with others, especially first-time moms, but at the same time I wish someone had adequately warned me about just how hard birth and recovery can be. I am sure that, had I known the facts of what to expect, instead of having a beautiful picture painted of the meaning of life and the holiness of birth, I would have responded differently. At the very least, I would have set up my environment differently.

Pushing gave me a rush and a real sense of productivity and achievement. When I saw my daughter for the first time, I felt privileged to provide for my husband, but I felt no sense of attachment to her myself. I didn't know what to do – I had been told to put her against my naked body, skin-to-skin, and feed her, but I was weak and drugged from the epidural and the exhaustion of extended labor. I was also surrounded by people cleaning up and going about their hospital business, so my gown was staying on! I had also never nursed before, so I had no clue what to do, and I was embarrassed to fumble my way around it in front of everyone. I allowed my baby to be taken to the nursery and I was wheeled to my room.

On the first day I had a rush of energy. I had no desire to see my baby, and it didn't occur to me that I should go get her from the nursery. No one brought her to me, and I figured I would soak up the time to myself and someone would let me know when she needed to eat. All the reading, all the listening, all the preparation…and it was like my head was full of sand.

I found myself completely panicked when my husband wasn't around. I felt that I couldn't reach out to anyone. My energy wore off and I felt pain. I couldn't believe how much blood kept coming out of me.

In the evening, a nurse brought me my baby. She said she was hungry and left. I did everything I could to get my baby to latch but she couldn't, and I couldn't teach her. She cried and I cried. No, I sobbed and looked up at the Heavens and begged for help. I went to the nursery and said I couldn't feed. They told me to keep trying. My baby was making sucking faces at me, and I was heartbroken. How could it not be the easiest and most natural thing in the world to provide basic sustenance for your child? I broke down in the nursery, and a nurse told me it was OK to give her formula. I told them to add to her chart that it was OK to give her formula at night and I would try again in the morning.

The next day a lactation consultant came by and apologized for forgetting to come to me the day before. I was in pain from the birth and had completely exhausted myself from crying so much the night before. I felt vulnerable and small and didn't have the energy to be angry. I let her show me tips for proper latch, and I nursed my baby. I kept her next to me all day and even put her on my bed so she could feel me nearby.

I got visitors, which I felt mixed about. On the one hand, I was so relieved to not be at home, and on the other hand, I couldn't bear for anyone to see me looking so pathetic. I could hardly hold it together.

By the next day I had forgotten how to nurse. It was the weekend, and there was no one to help me. It was day 3, so I became engorged as my milk really came in. I sat in my bed expressing by hand into a cup for relief.

I took my baby home that night. I blasted all the heaters to warm our home, borrowed a pump and formula, and cried some more for not knowing more in advance. I know what hormones feel like, and I knew that I was not just being emotional from hormones. I told my husband I was having a breakdown and I needed him to call people for help – I mentioned names of older women in our community. He made an appointment for a lactation consultant to come to our house in the morning, and we agreed he would give the baby a bottle. He sat with me while I fell apart and talked to me until I fell asleep.

There never seems to be enough sleep. Always tired, always in pain, always emotional. Even though I learned how to nurse, I hated it. I was petrified I would drop my baby on her head or pull her arms out of their sockets when dressing her. I was afraid to drown her in the bath. I was afraid she wouldn't eat enough. I was afraid that putting her on a three-hour schedule meant she wouldn't sleep enough.

Even though I was exhausted, I couldn't sleep. Even though I was starving because of the calories being burnt up nursing, I couldn't eat. I didn't answer my phone when people called. I asked women dropping off food to leave it in the kitchen and go, because I was busy. I didn't talk to anyone, except my lactation consultant.

She called me multiple times a day. She sent over day nurses and night nurses to help me, teach me, watch my baby so I could sleep. She explained to me that I didn't have to do everything "by the book" and that I could disregard a lot of the information I received from various books in order to help me calm down and establish my own routine for my baby (and myself).

In the second week, I took my baby to get her vaccines, and I broke down in front of the nurse.

She told me that if I couldn't or didn't want to nurse, my daughter would still be fine. She encouraged me to get a pediatrician so I would have someone to answer my questions. She encouraged me to sleep. She encouraged me to call her. And she encouraged me to go to my family in South Africa so I could have a support system. Which is exactly what I did.

In the third week of my child's life, I took her on a plane by myself to a different continent. The moment my mother looked at me, she told me we needed to see a doctor. She got me onto medication to help with the depression. She took us to a pediatrician so I could ask everything I wanted. She helped me bathe and dress my child, and she held her while I slept. I cannot say I was healed when I left, but I was definitely stronger. By week 4, my daughter smiled at me.

At week 6, I had to return to work. I was traumatized by the idea of leaving my child with a stranger, but felt like I had no other option. I was so afraid that people might know how weak I was. I was petrified of losing my job. I wanted to be superwoman and I was so frustrated with myself for not being able to be exactly that. I found a wonderful woman to watch my child near my office so I could slip out and nurse her twice a day. I had started to sleep again, and my daughter had a clear, set routine, which made me feel more capable of managing our lives.

It took me four months before I felt like myself again – before I loved my baby and appreciated that she is in my life. It took me four months to stop being overwhelmed and afraid. It took me four months, a therapist, two psychiatrists, and a change in medication to finally be able to feel the floor underneath me again.

I adore my daughter. I enjoy watching her grow, seeing her character develop, figuring out what she does and doesn't like. Every milestone is a mutual achievement. I am so much in love with her that I cannot imagine a life without more of her. I have decided I am ready for another child.

This time, things will be different. I would like to take a doula with me to the hospital. I plan to keep people around me who understand hospital-speak, so I will know what is going on and will be able to express my needs. My mother is coming here. I will call my lactation consultant as soon as I deliver to make an appointment so I'll know what I am doing from the start. I have the numbers of night nurses. I have already told my husband what I need from him, and how, and when. I know not to expect anything of myself based on what the books or other people say. I know I am a mother and that means I instinctively know what's best, and if that doesn't fit in with what I have been told, that is OK. I know whom to call on, and I have spent the last eighteen months of my life working on how to ask for help.

Children are a blessing. I feel like they are the truest way to get in touch with my own humanity. I know that many mothers don't experience the postpartum depression that I did, and I hope I will never experience it again. I try to make myself available to anyone who is having a difficult time postpartum – to refer them to the great people who helped me and to share what I learned to help them get to the other side.

Still Today

Four of us from our new mommies group continue to meet now, thirty-three years later.

KATHY T.
MOM
AGE 63 (31 AT THE TIME OF THE BIRTH)
FIRST BIRTH

The best of places and times, the most challenging of places and times... that's what I think I will start with. We were all sure that we were doing everything right. Most of my group of friends had been married several years, had our careers in place, and just about when we were thirty years old, or even a bit older, we decided this is the right thing to do... we are ready... I was ready! All kinds of knowledge and information on pregnancy and childbirth was available, yet all kinds of judgment and prejudice about doing it just the right way was there, too.

I ran and did calisthenics daily, I ate well, I had great friends and a wonderful husband. I took prenatal yoga, Lamaze (after exploring other options), and signed up for the new "ABC" Alternative Birth Center at the best baby hospital with everyone's favorite doctor.

All set and ready to go! I assumed all would go well, as I had done all the "right" things. So... baby comes about three weeks early... he was breech... I was not eligible for the ABC center because of the risk... it was suggested I have a cesarean... the epidural didn't work... the spinal didn't work... then they said I needed a general anesthetic (which I was told never happens anymore)... so out I went... and the baby came!

I was so sad and depressed and tired, I didn't even open my eyes to see the baby, even though my husband kept nudging me. Finally, I did.

The nurses and doctors were great... said I would stay for six days because of my C-section (way back then, they let you stay longer). I didn't want to change a diaper, or start nursing. My friends came, and I cried and cried.

They had been bringing the baby to me, but on day 2 (or 3?) I wanted him back in the nursery so I could rest. Finally at the end of day, the sweet nurse came to me and said, "Honey, I think it's about time you went and saw that baby of yours!" So I went to the nursery and had to read the names of the babies on the cribs to find mine! Then at that moment, I read his name, and saw my baby really for the first time, and fell in love.

But even though I was happy with him, I was depressed and stressed during the time in the hospital. Six days after the birth, they said I could be sent home. I was crying, confused, absolutely overwhelmed that they would send this baby home with me, as I didn't have a clue what to do.

First week home: I had given the baby too much sugar water in the hospital just to keep him from crying, and he had a hard time nursing and so did I.

BEST SUPPORTS FOR ME: I got into La Leche League in Berkeley, California, and although I was surprised to see so many toddlers nursing, the group supported and helped me get on track with nursing my newborn.

At five weeks postpartum, I joined a moms' group of seven moms in the neighborhood led by the renowned Sherry Reinhardt, a nurse practitioner in our neighborhood. She started running these groups of six to eight moms after she had her first child, who is two years older than my son. We met once a week to receive and build support, and share our stories.

Sherry did a formal group for two months. She provided structure and facilitation, as she was a master at this. After the two months, moms could choose to continue or not continue on their own. Four of us from the group continue to meet monthly to this day, thirty-three years later! I'm told this is unheard of... more on that later.

Eventually a couple of years after my son was born, I started entering therapy, investigating my family history of depression – my own mother's probably very severe postpartum depression after each of five births and no acknowledgment of what that might have been. Though not for everyone, taking mild antidepressants for my depression for a temporary time was key.

An acknowledgment of my family predisposition to depression and how this was particularly strong for me during hormonal times (menstrual cycle, postpartum, and then again at menopause) helped me make decisions that were helpful later on for me. NONE of this was really talked about or dealt with at the time.

HARDEST FOR ME: Again, there were lots of judgments and expectations before having the baby and after (even today I still see that).

Expectations were that you MUST have natural childbirth, you MUST nurse, you must be a supermom, you must NOT take medication, etc. These judgments generally came more from my peer group than from the medical community. The medical community did not address the issue of postpartum depression, maybe because I didn't ask... or more likely because it was not discussed as an issue in the early 1980s.

So when I couldn't have natural childbirth, and I had difficulty nursing, there was a judgment I think passed on us mothers who weren't the hippie ideal. I know this could be anywhere, but given the environment of Berkeley, California, it was probably worse. But as a peer group with strong opinions and judgments, we were also loving and understanding of each other as we became closer.

I did not live near family, so my friends, peer group, community, and therapy became supports. The best of Berkeley was that there were plenty of those supports available. I was in two moms' groups, baby massage, mom and me, etc., etc. It was so hard that I said, "I am only having one... but he is a fantastic ONE!" I always say I could be a great mom to one kid!

All seven of us in the group continued together for about six years. The moms' group became a playgroup as well as a support group. The moms would go off to Lake Tahoe once a year and leave the kids with the dads! Over the six years, many tragedies of life entered. Two divorces, moving away, my son had leukemia (doing well now, thankfully), one husband died tragically. I think those strains brought out the best and worst of friendships. Four of us really connected well, even though we were very different. We are the four who have continued for thirty-three years. Sherry used to say we were the longest-running moms' group in all of Berkeley (maybe the world?).

My moms' group is now Karen, Maria, Susan, and me. Three of us are grandmas. I remember when we all met at the first meeting, Susan had had a natural delivery and chanted through childbirth. Then all of us that had to have C-sections cried, because that's what we wanted. Susan is one of my best friends today, though I was so jealous of her childbirth. We all supported each other that first meeting about our disappointments or triumphs of childbirth. We helped each other with nursing issues, etc., though it was key to have our nurse practitioner there to start us off, since we didn't have a clue, and most of us did not have family nearby.

I remember one thing in particular - that by mistake I thought I read that babies weren't supposed to wear socks (the actual information was shoes), so I never put socks on my son, even in the cold! When I got to the meeting, I told the group that babies aren't supposed to wear socks. Sherry kindly shared with me that maybe socks are OK – just not shoes. Everyone laughed.

I didn't know how to wear my Snugli baby carrier. We were all so tired and confused. But that group helped get me through the first few days, weeks, months, and now, thirty-three years later we meet every month and talk about everything under the sun... politics, homes, friends... But number one, we talk about those babies who were six weeks old when we started and are all now turning thirty-three years old!

Sadly, Sherry passed away six years ago. At the time she had been the support facilitator to thousands of Bay Area new moms. She had a memorial which was attended by so many. I had to miss it but for the best reason – visiting my new grandchild.

I often share my birth story with my wonderful, now thirty-three-year-old son, and I say, "Well, I didn't take easily to motherhood and didn't do such a great job early on..." and he so sincerely contradicts me by saying, "But MOM, you are absolutely the BEST MOM anyone could ever have, and have always been."

Siblings: When Baby Makes Four (or More)

Family Anew

"Mommy," he murmured, just loud enough for me to hear,
"Don't forget about ME, Mommy."

Aimee W.
Mom
Age 42 (31 at the time of the birth)
Second of two births

Even though it was my second baby and I should have known what to expect, I was nervous and could not sleep. Part of the problem was general worry, but the other part was the planned cesarean section looming in the morning. I paced the hall, threw a load of laundry into the washer, and finally opened the door to my son's bedroom.

Bailey was just shy of three that June and generally a good sleeper. I had spent enough nights watching my firstborn just sleep to know that. This night, however, he awoke when I stood over his big-boy bed. "Shh," I soothed, "go back to sleep."

I bent down, kissed his brow, and moved toward the doorway. "Love you, big boy," I called softly.

"Mommy," he murmured, just loud enough for me to hear, "don't forget about ME, Mommy."

The tears leaked from my eyes in a rush of emotion. How did he know what was really going on? We had told him that his new sister was arriving the next day and that Nana and Pop-Pop were coming to take care of him, as were Grandma and Poppy.

We discussed how exciting it would be to come to the hospital to see me and the baby. He acted like he couldn't wait, helping us strap the infant seat securely into the car in readiness. Surely he didn't think we were replacing him, did he? I went back to the edge of his bed and sat there, my hand on his little arm, still crying, and whispering my love and my promise to of course "remember him," until I was sure he was asleep.

I did go back to my own bed eventually, but sleep was elusive.

My childhood best friend Bonnie was staying with us that night also. Her husband was taking care of their babies so she could come be with me. She had had two C-sections already, and when I told her a few weeks beforehand how nervous I was, she didn't wait for me to ask; she insisted on coming down to suburban Washington, DC, from her New Jersey home to be with me for the birth. Until then, there was no reason to believe that I wouldn't give birth naturally, like I had with Bailey. But this baby wasn't cooperative; she had turned breech at this eleventh hour, and between her size and my tiny stature, turning her wasn't going to be an option. So we planned the C-section.

Bonnie, Marc, and I left before Bailey awoke, leaving a babysitter in the house to give him breakfast and care for him until my in-laws arrived that afternoon.

Like many hospitals, George Washington University Hospital was already jumping at 6:30 A.M. The nurse quickly ushered us into a tiny room where I changed into a gown and we waited until the anesthesiologist was ready for me. Bonnie chattered at us. I don't remember what she said but she just talked, and we were grateful. Later she told us that we both looked so stressed that she felt compelled to chat to keep the air clear of those negative vibrations. When I get stressed, I get loud; when my husband is stressed, he gets overly quiet. Bonnie was having none of either extreme.

I wanted Bonnie to come with me to get the spinal anesthesia, but the nurse insisted I was better off alone and she would bring me right back. Marc and Bonnie waited in that little room.

They waited and waited and waited. I had forgotten to tell the anesthesiologist, a third-year resident, that I have scoliosis, a curvature in my spine. Every time she touched me, I flinched because she was having trouble getting the needle between my vertebrae due to the unexpected curve right where she wanted to push and poke. After the third unsuccessful try, she called her attending physician.

I didn't think the wait was overly long at that point, especially since the nurse told my husband and Bonnie that I'd be back in less than half an hour. But, it was nearly an hour before I actually returned, and they were really nervous waiting that long! I leaned back on the gurney in that little room, already panting with exhaustion, but no longer feeling anything from my waist down.

Once the head anesthesiologist had arrived, everything had gone smoothly and painlessly, even though the resident shot me a dirty look and reminded me that next time I needed anything done with my back I needed to tell someone about the scoliosis.

It was a short wait with both Bonnie and my husband with me until they whisked me off to the surgical suite to give birth. What a different experience! When Bailey was born, I labored for hours in a brightly-lit, flowery-decorated labor room, and then when I was ready, the doctors and nurses came to me, I pushed for a while and had a beautiful baby. That experience was not without its stresses; for reasons still unknown, Bailey was just over five weeks early and my husband and I had been on vacation in the Shenandoah Mountains. It wasn't urgent when my water broke, so we drove back to George Washington Hospital that night, but it was frightening to have our first baby so early when we were so unprepared.

Bailey was about five pounds and had terrible problems feeding. He had fluid on his lungs and he spent his first year on a nebulizer pretty much around the clock. The pediatric pulmonologist had told us that Bailey would either have asthma or outgrow the problems by the time he was two. Thankfully, it was the latter, and while my husband and I were scarred from the rounds of tests and doctors that comprised Bailey's first year, Bailey himself was unscathed. As we waited, I know we all hoped that since this baby was full-term, we would have none of the same issues.

Bonnie decided to stay in the room and let my husband accompany me to the surgical suite. They transferred me from the gurney to the table – and by "they," I mean at least four different people. I didn't know who anyone was, much less their roles. There was a stool by my head for Marc, and he sat on it. There were two "wings" off of the surgical table, designed to hold my arms so they would stay away from my body. I had a brief moment of panic – were they going to tie down my arms?

I promised to hold my arms still on the little wings and they agreed not to tie them there. Having my arms tied down felt like the ultimate humiliation and loss of control. I could hold my own arms, thank you very much.

After that, things were a bit blurry. I finally recognized someone in the room: my obstetrician, Dr. Powers – whom I trusted completely – came to speak with me and provide a reassuring touch to my shoulder before proceeding to the other end of me. Dr. Powers talked his way through the procedure, warning me whenever there might be something I would sense or feel. My husband kept one hand on my head or arm, but kept standing to see over the sterile drape, despite my protests. Gross!

In what seemed like just a few minutes, I could hear the baby give a first lusty cry. We had known it was going to be a girl, but hearing her for real just stopped my breath for a moment. "Bless you, welcome girl," I murmured.

With only the immediate smear cleaned off of her, the nurse placed the baby on my chest for a brief moment and I could feel the tears running down my face into my ears as I tried to lie as still as possible. She was perfect, this daughter of ours. My husband touched her, kissed my forehead, and told us he loved us. She was pink and round and perfect, and the nurse took her to weigh and swaddle her.

Bonnie had done me one other favor that day. She had had a bad experience with the staples in her C-section cut, and had warned me clearly. I had already discussed with Dr. Powers that he should use regular stitches, not staples, as he closed my wounded belly. In the end, I was thankful. I had no trouble with my incision, and it healed cleanly and quickly, unlike others I knew who had staples.

Bonnie stayed with Marc and me for the rest of the afternoon with our new daughter, and because of that day, she has always felt some sense of ownership of the baby who would become our feisty, sassy, and curly girl, Sydney. Bonnie and Sydney belong to each other, really, and it's clear to any outsider watching as they talk and move together - now eleven years later - that they have a special bond, and I am grateful for it. The more people who love my babies, the better off those babies are, I think.

The last bond of the day came later, when Marc's parents, who had been watching Bailey all day, brought him to the hospital to see his mom and meet his new sister. My parents would arrive the next day to see us through our homecoming.

Bailey didn't hesitate. Marc pulled off his shoes and sat him on the bed next to me, and with Bonnie and Marc on one side of him and me on the other, he held his baby sister on the day she was born. He kissed her head and called her "Bay-buh," a funny little name he would use for her first year, before dropping it and calling her simply "Syd." As for that infant, I swear she knew him. In the coming weeks she would always turn to his voice. He was the recipient of her first smile, and after a few days of separation weeks later, he got her first real laugh. While I was away in the hospital, they had missed each other.

Bailey beamed from that bed next to me. I think he finally understood, and I witnessed that understanding suffuse his beautiful little face. This baby had come out of his mommy (and from his daddy, too), but part of her was Bailey's, also. Even though he wasn't even three years old at the time, I am sure he instinctively understood the bond they shared. I figured it would happen – because people said it would – but until that moment, I don't think I fully understood how the heart can expand so completely to take in the love of, and for, another child. But Bailey showed us how to do it. On that day we became complete. On that day, with both of our babies together, we became our new family.

At Wits' End

Three months of that poor baby screaming her guts out, not growing, no attention or energy left for her older siblings, nasty floors, no sleep and sooooo much aggravation...

ANDREA D.
MOM, ARCHITECT, VIRTUAL ASSISTANT, WRITER
AGE 42
THIRD OF SIX BIRTHS

They said it wouldn't, couldn't happen – but it did, and we were thrilled! My first birth had brought me a perfect baby boy. And hypothyroidism. My second pregnancy only happened through patience and a dose of fertility medication, accompanied by a solid declaration that this was the only thing that would work for me. I made my peace with it, got a second, wonderful son, and went on with my life. Well, doctors can be wrong, and they were. With little guy number two thirteen months old, I was nauseous all over again. Fast forward through five months of nasty nausea and another, thank God, nearly perfect pregnancy that reached 41 weeks, 5 days. My daughter was born! That surreal first nursing in the delivery room went just fine, just as it had with my boys.

And then, she vomited. No, not spit up – a line I was to repeat hundreds of times over the next three months – vomit. And it continued, several times a day, accompanied by near-constant nursing, no weight gain at all, and crying and screaming on both mine and my daughter's accounts. It was called reflux, but at the time, it wasn't treated unless there was a weight loss involved. When my daughter was six weeks old and still at birth weight, I took her to a lactation consultant. This woman was sweet, kind, and patient, and had all kinds of things to say about nursing positions and what I was doing wrong. If I'd only hold her right, in a manner that was extremely uncomfortable and darn near impossible for me, she would nurse properly, gain weight, be happy, and do just fine. I left more befuddled than when I'd arrived.

I decided to go out every day to study in an architectural program. Yes, I wanted to get my degree and be qualified to do something more interesting than the here-and-there, mostly mindless employment that I'd held up until then. However, my real, unstated reason for suddenly having this need for educational stimulation was that I found this a "legitimate" reason to leave my screaming daughter in the care of someone else. I felt that the studies justified the expense. Why didn't I just feel that it was worth it to step away from her periodically for my own mental health? Why was that not a priority that anyone mentioned anywhere along the way? Maybe that's just the way it was in 2001 in my circles. I don't know.

When she reached three months old, and was still vomiting several times a day and much heavier than her birth weight, the pediatrician haphazardly remarked that we could just give her Gaviscon and be done with it.

What? Had I heard that correctly? Couldn't be. It must be the daze. I asked him for a repeat and he said the same thing all over again. Three months of that poor baby screaming her guts out, not growing, no attention or energy left for her older siblings, nasty floors, no sleep and sooooo much aggravation... can be solved by a bottle available at every Walgreens for $1.99? I would say I saw red, but I didn't. I saw Gaviscon. Lots of it.

We rushed out and got our Gaviscon. (Actually my mom did – thanks, Mom!) I'd nurse my daughter, then pour that milky blue potion into her. She liked it, so at least that part didn't involve additional torture. Only after we'd gotten the medication going as a regular routine did my daughter cease her screaming and start observing the world. I could finally catch my breath. I felt like a deficient mother when I could only state that I was starting to love my daughter when she was over three months old. What mother doesn't instantly love her daughter?

Life wasn't all flowers and rainbows right away, either. My eldest was four years old and being made fun of in kindergarten. My second son was two years old, and was having hearing problems. Child number three continued to grow, and even to flourish, but she did continue intermittent vomiting until she was in first grade. Life was rough, but while we all have our parenting ups and downs, I do want to share my light at the end of the tunnel. So here goes:

I'm glad I kept at it. I found that the single most important thing I do for our children is to advocate for them. Be it medical, social or educational issues, when I'm really present with them, it pays off. That eldest child who cried every day he went to kindergarten moved to another school system and is now seventeen years old, in his senior year of high school, and has a wonderful circle of friends. That second sweetheart, the one with hearing problems, he's still having hearing tests, but he's already started high school, loves it, and is making fantastic grades. And my daughter? She's a headstrong twelve-year-old, a math-loving achiever, master of her own babysitting empire, a gymnast, and yes, healthy! This is one mama who knows that there are going to be issues and that we will get through them. I just take a deep breath, hold hands, consult with every other mother on the playground benches, and continue to do my best to advocate for my kids, and forge onward!

VBAC Hopeful

It is so hard to talk about these things even to people you are close with, and yet it's so important to process, even years later, as the effects linger.

Renanit L.
MSW, nonprofit professional,
Postpartum doula and lactation counselor
Age 39 (34 at the time of the birth)
Second of two births

My second daughter was born on January 2, 2008. I had had such a difficult time after the birth of my first daughter, for which I had to have a planned cesarean. I had so many problems with breastfeeding, postpartum depression, and a really hard time bonding with my baby. I did everything in my power to avoid a similar experience the second time, and I set about planning for a VBAC (vaginal birth after cesarean).

I switched healthcare providers twice to have a better chance at a VBAC – the second switch as late as 34 weeks – to ensure my highest likelihood of avoiding another C-section. I hired a very experienced doula who had supported women through VBACs before. I read everything I possibly could to learn what to do and not do so I wouldn't have to go through the same thing again. I hired a baby nurse so I knew I could get rest after my birth and strengthen myself to avoid depression again. I gathered resources on postpartum depression so I could plan for a recurrence and recognize the signs the second time around. I planned and hoped for the birth I did not have the first time.

Then life intervened. My water broke at 10 P.M., two days before my due date. My midwife told me to try to get some rest. I slept soundly all night and woke up with no labor having started. I went to the hospital. They checked me, told me I was not dilated, then let me go. I went home, took castor oil as an induction measure (which did nothing at all for me), ate lunch, and called an incredible acupuncturist, who came to my house and gave me an amazing acupuncture treatment that kicked me into full labor by the end of the hour-long session. I went back to the hospital, was checked in, and everything proceeded exactly as I wanted it to for several hours. Everyone followed my birth plan, leaving me and my husband alone with lights off, music on, monitors turned down so far we could not hear or see them, with no interference or intrusions.

After a few hours of contractions, I suddenly sat up straight and said to my husband, "Something is not right." At that very moment, my nurse and midwife came running into the room, turned on the lights, and screamed that they needed to check me. They did, and they told me in very panicked voices that the baby's heart rate had been dropping for ten minutes very suddenly, and they had let it go as long as they possibly could, but the baby was in grave danger and needed to be born right away.

I had to have an emergency cesarean. They had a wheelchair to take me to the operating room. I refused it and walked across the hallway on my own two feet into the operating room, where they prepped me quickly. Unlike many so-called "emergency" cesareans, in which no one is really in danger, I could tell that this was a true emergency: people were running around and screaming and moving as quickly as they possibly could. From the moment they told me I needed surgery, to the moment my (healthy, robust) daughter was born, only eight minutes passed.

Despite the panic around me and the fear in my husband's eyes, I knew in my bones that my baby was fine, and I never worried about her for a minute. I had a much better hospital experience the second time around, as I much preferred the atmosphere and nursing support in the different hospital. I also hired a postpartum doula, who stayed overnight with me in my room and helped me initiate breastfeeding well. She also watched over the baby to allow me to get some rest. By the time I left the hospital, my milk had already come in and nursing was going relatively well, which was totally different from my first nursing experience, when my daughter didn't get a drop and I was severely engorged and in pain by the time we left the hospital.

We had a baby nurse stay with us for two weeks. Although at times it was awkward to have someone in our (small) home with us, and part of me felt bad that I was not doing everything for my new baby myself in those early days, it was also key in letting me rest. I had decided that if nursing was going well, I would pump and have the nurse give the baby a bottle in the middle of the night, allowing me to sleep for a four-hour stretch uninterrupted. This worked, and I felt almost like myself by the time the baby nurse left fourteen days after the birth. With the exception of some pain in the first week, I was eating and drinking normally, had a lot of energy, and was able to truly enjoy my baby right from the start.

Within just a few weeks, I was able to be active again, and when I accepted visitors at around three weeks postpartum, I was able to truly enjoy them, unlike with our first baby, when I could barely muster the energy and spirit to smile at guests. I was also better about asking for help: whenever anyone asked what they could do, I said, "Bring food!" Eating well during those first weeks really helped to get my strength back up and made me feel cared for.

Nursing went beautifully, and I was able to exclusively nurse my daughter. In fact, I continued to nurse her for eighteen months, even after returning to work when she was nine months old. I became much more of an attachment parent from the start, holding her close to me, keeping her in a sling and sitting for hours with her sleeping on me, something I never had the patience or desire to do the first time. Whereas after my first child was born, I wanted nothing more than to go back to work, the second time I went back reluctantly, and part-time.

My second birth was in no way the birth I desperately wanted for myself, and there are still times I'm angry about that. I shed some tears writing this, even though it's been more than five years. In the past few years, I've made a determined effort to get in shape, to gain strength and form in my physical body, and I think a lot of that determination has to do with wanting to reclaim my body after two unwanted surgeries. I've become a trained postpartum doula and lactation counselor with a special interest in working with women who've had cesarean births or other traumatic birth experiences. Helping other new parents through their experiences has helped me process some of my own.

Although the ultimate outcome in terms of my own birth was not what I wanted, I felt and still do feel empowered by the choices I made. I truly believe that what happened needed to happen and that I did everything within my power to control the situation. Ultimately, I just could not. I am thankful that I was in a setting where I could have the medical care I did and that my little girl was born fully healthy. I am thankful that my recovery was so much smoother and that I was able to ensure I could get back to my best self soon after the birth. And yet, five years later, I also can't get over the pain of it and the wish that things could have been different. I think the whole experience has made me much more compassionate, even though of course I wish things had gone differently.

I have showed my children my scars, and they often ask about their births. I have tried to leave them with no judgment or guilt about it, and I think it's worked, but I think it's also important for them to know something about it even at this young age.

It is so hard to talk about these things even to people you are close with, and yet it's so important to process, even years later, as the effects linger. I am really glad that I had the opportunity to write out my story.

Power of the Positive

Constant comments from outsiders, expecting the worst and assuming the worst, were tough. I kept wondering why people couldn't just let us be in our bubble.

Carol L.
Mom
Age 25
Second of two births

After the birth of my second son, I was a muddle of emotions, just like many other mamas. However, unlike with the birth of my first son, this postpartum experience I felt less like a live wire of roller coaster emotions, and more like, well, something less deadly. I had practiced HypnoBirthing during my pregnancy, and had a planned homebirth. The birth happened on my terms, in my comfort zone, which I know contributed to the crazy rush of strength and self-confidence I felt post-birth. With my first son, I felt small and worried, lying in my hospital bed wondering when I would get to see him again.

The first few hours after this second birth were bliss, just staring at the miracle lying in my arms. I couldn't sleep, overwhelmed by the desire to touch and cuddle this little smush of a human being. I remember thinking I had never felt so powerful and self-confident as I did in those first few hours. I was strong. I was radiant.

The first flicker of negative emotion that poked my little bubble of sunshine came from my husband. With my first baby I had an epidural and was quite calm, lying quietly in bed, detached and along for the ride. During this second birth, I was acting completely on instinct. I was on all fours, rocking back and forth, moaning and groaning like an animal about to pounce. I was screaming, urging myself on, and telling myself I could get through this even when I didn't feel I could. I think - because I was doing HypnoBirthing - he expected something similar to my first birth. Well, he wasn't the only one - but that's a whole other story.

In the first few hours, I didn't notice my husband's shock. He fell asleep while baby and I became acquainted and did some bonding. Afterwards, when we started talking about the birth, I asked him how he felt and how it went from his perspective. He said never again would we be doing a homebirth. My behavior had scared him. His reaction put me into a panic.

How could we have been at the same birth? Didn't he see what a beautiful, profound thing we had just gone through? No. His negativity toward the birth built in the days post-birth. Each time we talked about it we ended up fighting, and I'd end up sobbing like a two-year-old.

My mother was supposed to come in for the birth, but I had given birth before my due date, and she wasn't expected to arrive until two weeks later. In those days following the birth, my older boy was with my husband or mother-in-law. Those days, aside from the undertone of tension between my husband and me, were blissful. I would lie in bed nursing my baby and sleeping with him. When my older baby wasn't with my husband or mother-in-law, he was in bed with us, curiously touching the baby's hands and feet and planting overenthusiastic kisses on his head. Thankfully, he was just as in love with the baby as everyone else was. He easily accepted his new nursing partner, and would even hold his hand when they were both at the breast together.

Everyone kept asking, "Well, isn't he jealous?" Or if he wasn't listening, they insisted it was because he was jealous I was always holding the baby, and I needed to put the baby down more often in the crib. These constant comments from outsiders, expecting the worst and assuming the worst, were tough. I kept wondering why people couldn't just let us be in our bubble. Why was everyone trying to pop it?

My first weekend postpartum was stressful. My husband wanted me to relax and told me we would be going to his mother's house so she could pamper me and take care of the kids while I rested. I went into a panic and refused. The whole reason we went with a homebirth was so that I could recuperate at home. I was constantly showering, unable to take the burning when I peed. I was bleeding and just wanted the comfort of my own bed. I wanted my kids close, and I didn't want to be a guest. That was when my hormones finally caught up with me. He said I could never be conventional. It wasn't normal that I should want to stay home alone in my house postpartum. I should want to be surrounded by his family, having them do everything for me.

For hours on Friday I refused to go, and both he and his mother were trying to guilt me into changing my mind. I felt horrible. I was sure my husband would never forgive me for refusing to go, but I knew if I conceded and went there, I would suffer and I would not feel restful. I sobbed to my mother on the phone, completely torn about what to do. It felt like the biggest deal in the world, and I was overwhelmed and stressed. I kept trying to tell myself, "it's just the hormones," but it didn't help me feel any better. In the end we compromised and his mother and brothers all came to us, and his mother brought all the food.

My husband went back to work only four days after the birth, and so did my mother-in-law. I was so nervous that first day. Surprisingly, it went better than I expected. Physically, I felt energized and capable, but I was nervous about the logistics of taking care of two babies under two and that I would push myself, prolonging my bleeding unnecessarily. After all, I only had two hands, and I was afraid I was going to need four. Luckily I did have two more, belonging to one super-excited big brother.

My one-and-a-half-year-old became quite the helper, throwing out diapers, bringing me wipes, and cleaning up his toys. Less helpful was him trying to wipe the baby's spit-up with a dish towel, or trying to pull off the baby's umbilical cord stump, but hey, beggars can't be choosers.

It was tiring, to say the least, but definitely manageable. By the end of the day every drop of strength and patience had been squeezed from me, and I felt like a wrung-out sponge. I was too tired to cry but I cried anyway, half with pride in myself and half from pure frustration. With every day that passed, it got easier. I learned little tricks to keep things going smoothly. I also realized keeping the house decent was more important than keeping it spotless.

At the end of the day, I'd get into bed with both of my littles and the warm fuzziness of that moment, seeing them sleeping so peacefully together, made me remember why this job is worth all the hassle. I lived for those moments in the first few weeks. Waiting for those quiet times kept me going throughout the day.

Today, four months later, things are pretty much the same, although I'm much less tired. The crazy live-wire feelings have quieted down, and I no longer break out crying when I finally get to my coffee twenty minutes after I've poured it, only to discover it's barely lukewarm. For me, the hardest part has passed, and seeing my number two boy reach milestones and grow is just as exciting as it was with my first.

Two new things I've discovered during this postpartum experience are, firstly, I *can* in fact capably care for more than one child. Sometimes I think back to before baby number two was born and think about those good times when it was just me and my first, an inseparable team together. I can honestly say I miss those days. For me, that's OK. I know there are better days ahead of us with our new little addition.

A Support System

The day after our second child was born, my in-laws all came and visited me in the hospital, which was incredibly overwhelming and absolutely NOT what I wanted, but what could I say?

Rachel L.
Mom
Age 26
Second of two births

My name is Rachel. I have two girls who were born on May 27, 2011, and December 8, 2012. My second birth went really well. I wanted to wait until the absolute last minute to go to the hospital because I didn't want to deal with being in labor and the stresses of them pushing procedures on me that I didn't want. Well, it worked – I delivered my daughter naturally after only one hour. The biggest con of my birth was the care after giving birth. The bed wasn't comfortable, and I had to share a room. Also, the staff wasn't considerate and constantly left the door to my room open. They talked on the phone, and one nurse even used our restroom.

The first few months after she was born were incredibly hard for me. Unlike my first pregnancy when I was living near my own mother, who often visited to help, this time, we lived near my in-laws, who were not very helpful. With my first daughter, my parents lived a mile away from us and we routinely went over there for dinners during the week as well as on the weekends. My dad worked very close by, so I had lunch with him about once a week and also had lunch with my grandmother and my aunt a few times a month. We would go over to my aunt's house for dinner a couple of times a month as well. My sister even came over every once in a while to visit us. As you can see, beyond all the help with meal prep, I also had a lot of family that I could talk to and visit with. I also had a car. Overall, I didn't feel alone.

After my second child was born, my husband's family lived about the same distance away, but I would go a week without seeing them. The day after the birth, they all came and visited me in the hospital, which was incredibly overwhelming and absolutely NOT what I wanted, but what could I say?

In the first few weeks home from the hospital, they made attempts to help. We stayed with my mother-in-law for a weekend. My sister-in-law told us once that she was bringing over dinner, but at the last minute she canceled on us. She didn't even work at the time, yet she never came over to visit. My mother-in-law worked very close to our apartment, yet she never made the time to come before or after work to see us. We got very little help. I think the biggest shock was in the comparison - in our expectations from our experiences with our first, we hoped for and expected help since even though it was a different family, there were still as many people who could have helped. The problem was that they didn't.

I healed much quicker the second time, but the stress of having a one-and-a-half-year old and a new baby and not having much help were a lot not just for me but also for my marriage. Not to mention, the baby seemed to cry most of the time and we had a very hard time getting her to sleep (we still do sometimes). When she was around two or three months old, I began to wonder if what I was feeling was postpartum depression or baby blues. I just remember feeling such pressure to be the perfect mommy. No one talked to me about depression, so I didn't know what to watch out for. I remember rocking my baby for hours on the porch, imagining throwing her off, and maybe I'd just jump together with her and what would happen, break a leg? Arm? Die? Neck snap? How would I feel if she died? I never felt anything about it. I would just cry while I rocked her and rocked her and rocked her. Not because I was sad or happy, but just because.

Half the time I wouldn't realize I was crying, and other times I would be crying because I just wanted to sleep. It took me a while to really love her. I basically dealt with it on my own. My husband knew something was wrong, but I wouldn't let him do anything because I felt that I needed to be supermommy, and supermommy does everything, is never tired, has supper ready on time, etc. I had nervous breakdowns – I'd throw pots full of soup and break them, then sit down in the mess. I ended up realizing the probable cause of my hormonal madness: bad side effects from the birth control pill I was taking. I was clued-in enough to know that it was not OK to feel this way and I needed a break from those pills. I didn't realize just how crazy I was until after I stopped taking them.

Even with the craziness gone after quitting that birth control pill, I still felt exhausted, in fear of the strains on my marriage, worried and guilty that I was doing something wrong with my newborn, frustrated when I couldn't console her or when she refused to eat (for the first three months, she constantly fussed as she nursed), and confused as to what to do to fix any of these problems.

Before giving birth, I had seen a psychologist to help with the stresses of relocating, and after the birth my mother-in-law and husband convinced me that I should see a psychiatrist. So I did. I told her that I wasn't sure if I was depressed or just exhausted and a bit overwhelmed. I kept trying to explain how I felt – I felt all the feelings I mentioned above, but I never lost hope that things would one day get better. Every time I started to explain the feeling, she cut in with a comment that insinuated that I was depressed, yet that was not how I felt.

Honestly, I was too exhausted to argue with her, and the

thought of a little pill making me feel better sounded amazing. As soon as I walked out of her office, though, I realized that something was wrong with the picture. I tried taking the medicine but I could never remember, and when I went back to see her a few weeks later, I honestly told her that I hadn't managed to take it much but I was feeling better because my baby was sleeping better. You know what she said? She said that I still looked depressed. I stopped listening to her after that and decided that she wasn't going to help me.

A few weeks after that, I went back to the psychologist that I had seen before giving birth and told her about all of my feelings, and she listened. She didn't cut in. She didn't add her perspective. She then told me that everything I'm feeling is normal. She told me (because she knows me) that she doesn't think I am depressed but rather going through a difficult time. She said that she recommends I either continue coming to see her or find someone else who can help me get through it.

My daughter just turned four months old. Things still aren't perfect. I still wake up some mornings exhausted. I still have moments when I get frustrated. I still have days and nights when I wonder when this will get easier. But now most of my time is spent smiling, and sometimes my daughter smiles back.

Right now, the idea of getting pregnant again is frightening. I don't think we could handle a third child. I don't know what we'll do for future births, but I think that we are going to have to enlist more help from family, and hope next time they will be more willing to help and we are more prepared.

It's funny, but just writing this seems to have had some sort of calming effect. Like I've finally been affirmed for all the conflicting and confusing feelings I had.

Empowered

When my baby slid out from my body, I was the most powerful woman in the world.

Amanda E.
Early childhood educator,
children's party entertainer, stay-at-home mom
Age 36
Fourth of four births

My third birth was a nightmare. I ended up knocked out, strapped down to a table while they tugged my (head-down) baby from a cut in my abdomen. It was traumatic, and when I discovered twelve months later – despite numerous, simultaneous birth control methods – that I was pregnant again, I cried.

But I was also convinced that the trauma of an out-of-control birth would never happen to me again. I steeled my will and began exploring VBAC options. I had nine months to make myself an expert on how I could get back to giving birth normally. My first two experiences, both vaginal births, weren't what I would call phenomenal, but still so much better than a C-section.

So I found the most experienced doula for VBAC I could, herself a VBAC mom. I called hospitals and bugged doctors. I convinced myself that I would do this and beat the statistics. And I did, with much help from my wonderful doula, Anna, my husband, and even more importantly, my mother, who was able to come from thousands of miles away and finally witness one of my births.

When my baby – a four-kilogram (8 lbs., 13 oz.) redhead – slid out from my body, I was the most powerful woman in the world: I had beaten the odds of being a VBAC mom. And in doing so, with my own mom as a witness at the birth, I had made her one of the happiest women on the planet.

I had some issues with the hospital staff in the nursery. Because the baby was "so big," they were convinced she was diabetic and they said I had to supplement with formula (which I finally did under HUGE pressure, just because I wanted to get the baby away from them). They actually threatened to call social services if I tried to check the baby out of the hospital against medical advice. It was pretty frustrating to feel caught between two things I valued: getting home as soon as possible after a birth, and exclusively breastfeeding. When I finally came home from the hospital, I still had all the icky parts of being postpartum: the bleeding (fortunately no tearing this time!), the hormones intermittently making me crazy, including some of the normal (for me) feelings of depression. But because I felt so triumphant about this birth, I also had much more calm than previous returns home from the hospital after giving birth.

Considering I came home to a one-year-old, a three-year-old, and a four-year-old, it seems unlikely that I would use the word "calm" to describe anything in my life, but having the birth I wanted made me feel so... empowered – it was like the best drug ever. I was fortunate to have my mom around full-time for a couple of weeks after as well. By this point she knew the drill. She is a pro at doing errands, getting the kids to pre-school, etc. All I had to do was cook (which I love and would NEVER let anyone else do if I'm at all capable) and be with the baby. After my mom left, it was more difficult, because my husband also had to return to his job, and I needed to reestablish our family routine without Grandma.

We used disposable plates for a while (dishes are my most

hated chore!) and the house was even MORE of a disaster than normal (the floors didn't get washed for several weeks), but I was able to focus on my great birth and think, "If I can do that, I can do this also!" I kept my head above water, mostly, but I spent a LOT of time bailing the water, especially the first few weeks after birth.

Due to my experience of the VBAC, I became more like an ocean liner, able to plow through the waves with impunity even with all the hectic trials of managing four children ages four and under. The strong winds pushed me one way or another somewhat, but I didn't feel so constantly buffeted by the daily demands of motherhood.

The Need for Trust

Instead of receiving help, or encouragement, or sympathy for having such an experience, I was criticized and made to feel like a child.

SARAH B.
CHILDBIRTH EDUCATOR
AGE 25
SECOND OF TWO BIRTHS

As a childbirth educator, I hope that sharing my postpartum experience may help other women to validate their own postpartum feelings and learn more about this transitional time we all go through as mothers.

My labor started during the day, and my baby girl was born at 2 A.M. that night. I had a wonderful birth. It was a planned homebirth with my best friend and my husband both supporting me one contraction at a time. I was in control and at peace.

My immediate postpartum experience was another story, and the downturn really began the day of my labor. I had called my midwife several times throughout the day, updating her on how my contractions were progressing, fifteen minutes apart, ten minutes apart, seven minutes... I think my midwife didn't believe that I was in true labor, though, for whatever reason. Maybe it was because I had not seen my mucus plug come out, or because I sounded so calm on the phone... I don't know.

Despite my contraction times showing obvious progression

of labor, she didn't seem to believe me, because even though it would take her at least an hour and a half to get to my home, she didn't see the need to come until I told her my contractions were five minutes apart. I feel this was irresponsible and unforgiveable for an experienced midwife who was given ample warning and knew she was working with a woman in her second birth (which is likely to go quickly) who lived a significant travel-distance away from her.

It happened that I called her that last time at 12:30 A.M. to report contractions were five minutes apart. She finally came – seven minutes too late, after my baby was born. I was perfectly calm and trusting in her and believing in natural birth, but postpartum, I can only be grateful that my baby came out healthy without any need for extra medical attention. It was hard to know exactly how I felt immediately after the birth. It took time for everything to soak in, but when it did, I was upset that the midwife was paid in full, and upset and hurt that she didn't even apologize.

Thus began a most trying postpartum experience. One person in my family was most upset with me – as opposed to being upset with the midwife – for being alone without a birth professional at my birth. The day after my birth, this family member berated me mercilessly for "my" stupidity and irresponsibility and more. Instead of receiving help, or encouragement, or sympathy for having such an experience, I was criticized and made to feel like a child. This was the worst part of my postpartum experience, and even though I was happy for my beautiful, healthy baby girl, I was sad, angry, deeply hurt, and humiliated in front of my husband. Physically, I just felt tired and hungry, though not as sore as after my first birth, but emotionally, I was torn down and low.

This experience had a terrible effect on my marriage. The circumstances around my daughter's birth also made my husband feel like a failure and caused my husband to doubt me and my choices as the mother of our children. We have mended our relationship since then, but in addition to being very harmful to our relationship, it did not help us get off to a good start as new parents a second time around. I think we both felt as if there was an immense distance between us for some time, even though we were living in the same house. This lasted for several weeks. I felt inadequate as a mother and as a wife, perhaps even more so than I felt after my first birth, when being a mother was completely new to me.

I do remember some things that consoled me, though. Being a new mother all over again and holding my baby for the first time... being the first to pick her up and put her on my abdomen and watch her attempt the breast crawl... watching my curious older son get to know his little sister... having homemade food brought by two good friends... having the reassurance and encouragement from my best friend that I was being a good mother and that birth circumstances were not my fault.

Two weeks after my birth, it got even harder when my baby girl started showing signs of reflux and wouldn't nurse well during different times of the day. I had had trouble nursing my son, so when I also had trouble with my daughter, it was very disheartening. I had hoped it would be better this time – I'd hoped for a better start – but we can't always plan that out. Despite our best efforts, we can't control what happens to us, only our responses to each situation. With this new challenge, I felt even more inadequate in caring for my daughter.

I remember one thing that happened about five weeks after my daughter was born. I left my daughter with a relative so I could go out for a couple of hours to a wedding we had been invited to. I worried about not being with her the whole time, how she would be during her colicky hour, and whether she had enough breast milk in the bottle. Upon my return, this relative told me, as if it was news to me, that she liked to be held this way and how she liked her pacifier and how her colicky hour went and how to soothe her. I know the person meant well, but

I couldn't help but feel upset, as if I couldn't discover what my daughter liked and what comforted her. I sat and listened and felt more like a child than a mother.

Another challenge after my daughter's birth was meeting my son's needs for extra attention. My daughter was born in the summer, and my son was home from preschool for weeks 3 through 6 postpartum. The most challenging time of day was when I needed to nurse the baby, or when she needed to go to sleep and my son always wanted to be right next to me. I wish I had understood my son better and known how to help him. I wish I had trusted my daughter to learn to go to sleep without perfect silence, and I wish I had been more patient with my son those first months. I think I knew that we both needed extra love and comfort to understand our new place, but, looking back, I realize that without much mothering for myself (my mother lives in another country), I felt empty and didn't have that extra love to give him.

I cannot undo the past, but I hope I have learned to plan a little better for my next birth and to be at least a little more patient with myself, my children, and my husband. The most important thing for me as a mother after birth is to feel loved and refreshed, and to be able to find the strength to give the love that I want to be able to give to my family. I hope, for all mothers, that we can find the strength and support we need to be the best mothers we can be.

Of Many Homes

I was staying with family, with no place of my own, no real definition to my life, and a sense of not being in control of much that was going on.

CAITLIN F.
HOMESCHOOL MOM, WRITER, PERSONAL CHEF
AGE 29
SECOND OF TWO BIRTHS

When I was 36 weeks pregnant, I moved back to my husband's hometown, alone with my almost four-year-old son, Ben. Since the baby was due around the time that my husband would finish his previous job, we decided I should go on ahead with our son and get settled before the birth - my husband would fly out later. So my son and I spent the week after our arrival in New Jersey with my in-laws, then moved to my dad's house. His wife had passed away in their home a little over a year before, so it felt very poignant as we planned a homebirth there.

My greatest immediate sadness in moving away from where I had spent most of my pregnancy was leaving behind my trusted midwife and beloved friend, Leigh. She and I had grown quite close, as had our families, during the time we lived across the alley from each other. We had so many intimate conversations, alone and in our women's support group sessions. It seemed almost unthinkable to leave behind my birth plan with her, but thankfully she was from the same area in New Jersey where I was staying, and I was able to transfer my care to her midwife mentors, who were also her close friends. They welcomed me with open arms and hearts, almost as a piece of the friend they had been missing and longing for themselves. It was an honor to meet and work with them.

After my first birth, a hospital birth, where I felt like I kept waiting for something to happen to me, I was really determined that this would be MY birth. I would follow my body, and I just wanted everyone to leave me alone. I knew that my husband had felt very left out of the first birth, so I made an effort to stay open and communicate with him, allow myself to rely on him, and let him be as present as I was comfortable with. He really appreciated it. (He also accidentally filled the birth pool with cold water instead of very warm water, so there was a bit of frustration around that, but we worked through it.)

The birth started slowly, then progressed quickly. I gave birth in the birthing pool - a water birth. When my daughter was born, she was a bit blue and didn't breathe at first. The midwife patted her on the back, then waited a few seconds, and she eventually took a breath. I don't know how long passed, but it felt like forever. I kept saying, "Is she OK? Is she OK?" My midwife was so calm, she said, "She's OK, she's OK." Still in the birth pool, I held my baby in a towel, and then there was a big gush of blood, followed by the placenta. I tried to get out of the pool, but there was a lot of blood. It turned out that the placenta had partially detached as my daughter was born, starting a lot of bleeding. Then after it came out there was a huge gush and clot of blood. I felt super drained and light-headed. I was extremely nauseated, I had a bad headache, I was dizzy, I didn't have that endorphin "high" I felt after birth the first time. All I could do was lie in bed and try to weather the strong afterpains. My friend and midwife, Leigh, had watched the birth over Skype, and I felt happy that she was there with us, even as I was dizzy and distracted.

The midwives gave me herbs and homeopathic remedies, and handled the hemorrhaging. They fed me. They took care of all the after-birth business (weighing, measuring, cord cutting, etc.), and I don't really remember what was going on. My dad and Ben came in after our daughter was born, and my dad took her – all wrapped up – downstairs for a few minutes while the midwife stitched my tear. She was very meticulous and said the way she did it wouldn't leave a scar (which was true), but it was extremely painful, much more so than the doctor's swoop-swoop-done after the first birth. I remember she kept apologizing every time I winced, and I kept thinking, "Just do it and get it over with!" I wanted her to be more confident, and help me through it that way, instead of me having to keep saying "It's OK" every time she apologized.

I felt super exhausted after the birth, a bit better the second day after, and terrible with a really bad headache the third day. I took a lot of herbs, which I think helped. I passed a few egg-sized blood clots over the couple of days after the birth, and I actually passed a piece of placenta that had apparently "gotten lost" inside. My midwife was surprised because she said she had very carefully checked the placenta itself for any missing pieces before she encapsulated it. I was just thankful that it passed without any complication or infection, and wondered if that was part of why I felt so awful afterward.

I remember my overwhelming feeling after my daughter was born, especially as the days went on, was of being adrift. I talked it through with my midwife friend who has five children, and she reassured me that it is something that all mothers go through when we have a new baby. We aren't experiencing that intense and constant newness of becoming a mother for the first time, but we are going through a huge transition of becoming a mother of two or three, etc. I was also staying with family, with no place of my own, no real definition to my life, and a sense of not being in control of much that was going on. In certain ways it was peaceful, because I didn't have much responsibility outside of my new baby. It was also kind of scary and lonely, because I had left behind my support network. I was honestly particularly sad to leave behind the two weeks of home-cooked meals delivered to us, as was the custom in that community.

I hadn't had cable TV in the previous five years, so I spent most of the first month of my daughter's life lying in bed watching the Food Network or Home and Gardens channels, and nursing. My daughter didn't have trouble latching on, but my nursing was extremely painful for the first few days after she was born. On the fourth day, I saw that a sort of callus had developed on my nipples, then peeled off, and after that it didn't hurt anymore. It seemed strange, but I was grateful that we were healing and growing together.

My husband wasn't working yet, so he was with my son most of the time and I just focused on the baby. This made my life relatively easy in many ways, and I know that when we have another child (God willing), it will be very different to have to care for the two older children who are homeschooled in addition to a newborn!

My midwife friend helped me the most, by doing my postpartum visits, spending the time to really talk with me about how I was doing and feeling, giving me herbs to speed the healing of my body inside and out (they really shortened the bleeding), and bringing home-cooked meals to us many times. She really saved me at a time when I literally had no friends to support me. My husband was also supportive in many ways, but he was quite overwhelmed with my son and getting ready for our impending move for his job at a summer camp for a month, then to Miami to begin his full-time job. All the transition looming on the horizon made the first six weeks a sort of blissful haze of nothing going on, yet we struggled with anticipatory anxiety. For about three months, from the time we arrived in New Jersey, we had the constant feeling of waiting for something to happen.

Honestly, it sounds silly but I think watching the upbeat TV shows is what kept me from getting really depressed. I was lonely, so I focused on bonding with my baby and enjoying the beautiful natural surroundings of the lake where my dad lives.

My one regret is not being able to integrate my son into any sort of routine with me and the baby right away because of our strange living situation. My hope for our next child, God willing, is to bring my older children into the intimate experience of life with the baby right away, little by little, so we are all part of it together.

Angel Baby

The question of whether to have a third child lingered in my mind for years. I could never quite let it go.

Abby F.
Director, college prep program for low-income students
Age 41
Third of three births

Awe, delight, and love are the best words I can find to describe my postpartum days. I was in awe of my sweet, snuggly daughter nestled on my chest. I couldn't stop looking at her beautiful face. I loved the feeling of her squished up against the *outside* of my body, and I was filled to the brim with love and joy, watching her eight- and eleven-year-old brothers fall head over heels for her. I was just so grateful that she was alive and healthy.

Almost eight years after the birth of my second child, and over a year and a half after I decided it was now or never for number three – that yes, I did want to go for it – I discovered I was pregnant. I had been doing the "It's obviously not happening, I should move on... Well-maybe-we'll-just-try-for-one-more-month" head game, and was reaching the point of deciding it was time to start using birth control again because after all I was already forty and my boys were seven and ten, and I didn't want to risk being any older or having an even bigger gap between my kids. Even though it was hoped for, the pregnancy was a shock. And then, at my first prenatal appointment, it wasn't clear if the pregnancy was even viable.

When I got past that uncertainty, I went on to anxiously await CVS (chorionic villus sampling) prenatal diagnostic test results, assuming deep down at every turn that I would get bad news. But the pregnancy persisted healthily. I continued to hold the pregnancy at arm's length, afraid to get too excited or attached, knowing that I could carry full term and still not end up with a live birth. In the eight years between numbers two and three, I knew four women who lost full-term babies. Two stillbirths at 38 weeks. One baby who died during birth. One fetal death at 34 weeks. I was haunted by these stories. It became clear that it wasn't just poor women in the bush somewhere who lost babies, but also upper-class women who had access to the best medical care, prenatal yoga, and organic diets. I knew it could happen to me.

They say third births are a wildcard. Second babies come faster and easier than first ones, and with the third, you don't know what you'll get. At 35 weeks my baby was breech. If that's not a wildcard, I don't know what is. While mentally preparing myself for a scheduled C-section, I had appointments with a chiropractor, an osteopath, and an acupuncturist, and I took a homeopathic remedy. To my great relief, some combination of treatments helped my little one turn head down, and I was able to have a vaginal birth.

My labor started with my water breaking, something I had not experienced with either of my first two. About thirty minutes into mild, middle-of-the-night contractions that I was resting through, there was a burst, and I was soaked. I was eager to get to the hospital, because my boys came fast. I also found it stressful to be at home with continual gushes of fluid exiting my body, because I was GBS positive and anxious to start the antibiotics before the baby came out. My assumption was that I didn't have that many hours to work with.

But I was in for a much longer labor than I imagined, based on my previous two births, and I could not have made it through without my amazing doula. (I had not had a doula previously and am so grateful my husband had the wisdom to suggest it this time.) I labored for thirteen hours, with over two hours of pushing, whereas with both of my boys I went from 6 cm to delivery in two hours. I was mostly in a zone, unaware of time, swaying, moaning, even walking with my eyes closed. At times I fantasized about an epidural. I lost my romantic notions about labor and birth and simply thought it was f*ng hard work. I pushed in every imaginable position but none seemed to do the trick. Finally I had an episiotomy and Elia made her debut at 3:39 in the afternoon on May 2, 2013. She came out sunny-side-up (posterior), with a big bruise on her forehead. She had turned head down, but hadn't managed to get herself positioned for an optimal exit, which may have explained the longer labor. Thankfully, we both persevered through the challenge and she was healthy, strong, and alive.

I was in utter disbelief – that I made it through, that she was alive, that she was a girl after two boys, that we had a baby. It was all so overwhelming and joyful. With clarity, I pronounced, "That was so hard! That was officially the hardest thing I have ever done!" It was harder than birthing my first two children, harder than running a half-marathon or completing a triathlon. It was so damn hard, and I was so glad it was over, and I was never doing it again. Full stop. My family was complete. I was complete.

I was grateful for the supportive and noninterventionist doctors and nurses who were part of the birth. After Elia was born, she stayed on me, skin-to-skin, for over an hour before anyone bathed or weighed her. And for the two days we were in the hospital, I often snuggled her skin-to-skin, tucking her inside my pajama shirt. It was cozy and sweet.

I was lucky to have a strong, loving, and supportive family and community. Honestly I can't imagine having a baby without that. Meals, visitors, and carpool driving were indispensable, and for the first eight weeks of baby's life I had almost constant companionship. My husband took a few weeks off from work. My sister came for a week. My mom came for three weeks. And I had two older boys who had baseball games and end-of-school-year festivities, so I was out and about with baby from the beginning.

Since my daughter was born, I have told friends that she is the baby you would want to order from a catalog. She has these mythical qualities that I had heard about but didn't believe existed in real life. For starters, she sleeps. After having boys who awoke every two hours, suddenly I had a baby who slept for three or four hours at a time. There were even nights when she slept for six beautiful, continuous hours. It was rare that I was up more than twice a night. And that felt to me like a true miracle. To make it even more amazing, it was not hard to get her to go to sleep. I discovered by accident one day when I put her down to go to the bathroom that she could in fact fall asleep on her own if she was swaddled. That simple, miraculous fact eliminated the interminable holding, walking, bouncing, rocking, singing, arm-tiring, back-aching "if you don't go to sleep now I will literally lose my mind" aspect of new parenthood.

Within a few weeks after the birth, it became crystal clear to me that the secret to a happy life, and certainly to happy new motherhood, is sleep. It's hard to say how much of my post-partum bliss resulted from the happy hormones I got during pregnancy, which stayed with me after the birth, and how much was the result of having a magical baby who was an easygoing, long-sleeping (and incidentally, non-spitting-up) creature. Perhaps my postpartum bliss stemmed from the depth of my awe, gratitude, and delight at having a healthy third child at age forty (and turning forty-one ten days after her birth). Perhaps it was the added delight of having a daughter after two boys. Upon reflection, I'm sure it was a combination of all of these factors, and I am grateful for each one.

I'm someone who likes having clarity. The question of whether to have a third child lingered in my mind for years. I wanted it and I didn't. I could come up with solid arguments for and against. But I could never quite let it go. And I'm so glad I didn't. My daughter has brought so much joy to our family, and there is something in me that now feels content and fulfilled at a core level. I feel so grateful for her presence, her snuggles, her smiles, and her adoring eyes.

Unusual Circumstances

This Time Twins

I hired a few girls to come help me – not a single one lasted more than half an hour.

MIRIAM G.
MOM
AGE 34
FOURTH OF FOUR BIRTHS

I did a lot of research before I had my twins. It turns out I did a lot of the wrong research. While I focused on ways to convince my doctors to let me have a vaginal delivery, I failed to research what complications could occur, and which situations necessitated a cesarean, and then how to stand up to the doctor to prevent unnecessary surgery. I also thought that since I had breastfed my previous children, I would have no difficulties nursing my twins. I was wrong.

I went to a chiropractor trained in the Webster technique to help turn my transverse baby B. Baby A was head down, but unless both babies were head down, there were only three hospitals in my general area that would let me attempt a vaginal delivery. The closest was over an hour away.

Based on my previous births, I should have had no trouble. I knew how long I labored, I knew how to work through contractions. Since 37 weeks is the cutoff date for identical twins who share a placenta (they told me that after 37 weeks the placenta, which is severely taxed by double duty, starts to break down and the rate of stillbirth rises exponentially), I went into the hospital for a checkup. My blood pressure had skyrocketed and they were afraid I was becoming preeclamptic, so I got induced, and things went downhill from there.

This is where a bit of research might have helped. I thought that it would be better to break the water as a more natural form of induction, as opposed to using a synthetic means like Pitocin. It turns out, baby A didn't like having her amniotic sac ruptured. Her heart rate kept dropping, and I wasn't thinking clearly enough to ask the doctor to let me labor in a different position, or to wait with the C-section. I wanted to just get up and leave the hospital, and come back when I was ready to deliver. But I was afraid. So, on to the "emergency" C-section it was.

I'm now nine months postpartum, and the thought of their birth, and the unforeseen complications it would cause, still brings me to tears. I haven't yet figured out a way to come to terms with their birth and my subsequent difficulties in breast-feeding, which I strongly attribute to the cesarean.

One hour after entering the operating room, my baby girls were born. The weight-estimation ultrasound that I had three weeks prior was WAY off. Instead of both of my girls being close to the normal three kilograms (6 lbs., 10 oz.) and within one hundred grams of each other, they were tiny and had about a two-pound difference between them. But they were perfect. And yes, I didn't get to see them until four hours post-birth. I had a bad reaction to the medications they gave me, and those two hours in recovery were what I would assume a "bad trip" would be like.

When I finally made it back to my room after delivery, it was about 6 P.M. My husband brought both girls to the room. As I had done with my previous three births, I chose to have full rooming in. I can't even remember those first few hours, just that I wanted to breastfeed both girls, but was stuck in bed with an IV and magnesium drip that made me dizzy, and a cut-open abdomen. I couldn't reach into the bassinets from bed, so I had to get out of bed to lift up my girls. To make matters worse, the bed wasn't adjustable electrically – only manually – which meant that for me to lower or raise the back of the bed, I had to get out of the bed and do it.

At 8 P.M. the staff told my husband he had to leave – it was hospital policy that not even the father can stay past evening visiting hours. He wasn't allowed to stay and help me. I was on my own.

I'm pretty sure the nurses were helping me throughout the night. I can't really remember. All I know is that at some point I got tired of getting up to put babies back in bassinets, and one of them ended up sleeping with me in bed. I didn't get much sleep, because it's hard to sleep in those uncomfortable beds in an uncomfortable position, and I just didn't have the energy to get on my knees to find the lever under the bed to raise or lower it to a new position.

The next morning my husband came back at about 10 A.M. He stayed until 3, when he went home to take care of our other children. Days 3 and 4, he didn't return to the hospital, as unfortunately the family members whom we were relying on to help with our other three children were unable to do so properly.

The lactation consultant came to see me and immediately told me that I would need to supplement with formula. She said nothing like, "By the way, there is a pumping room you can use to start to increase your milk supply," or, "Here's a good way to position them so you can tandem nurse," or, "Good for you for wanting to nurse!"

Day 3 of our stay: the nurses must have complained to the doctor about my resistance to supplementing, because they called me in for a consult. The doctor looked at my babies' weights and told the nurses to back off.

My days in the hospital were spent nursing and trying to sleep a bit. Had it not been for the stitches, I would have been home on day 2. The nurses were all very nice, but once you were past the twenty-four hours post-birth, they had other people to deal with and didn't really have time to help the ones who had been there a while. Meanwhile, my girls were shredding my nipples due to undiagnosed tongue ties and incorrect latches. My milk was not coming in due to the C-section, stress, and an improper suck.

At some point I gave in and sent my girls to the nursery for a few hours so I could sleep and shower. I'd send them with the bit of milk I'd collected from my pumping sessions, always to the nurses' comment: "That's it? That's not enough for them to eat." So instead of resting, I'd go back to the room and try to pump some more. And then get called back to the nursery to get my "inconsolably crying" babies, who would be fast asleep when I got there and then continue to sleep for the next two hours. I got yelled at by the nurses for leaving my babies unattended in my room while I quickly went to the bathroom. Supposedly, I should have brought them back to the nursery instead of leaving them alone. It was seriously exhausting being in the hospital with no support from anyone and taking care of two newborns full-time while feeling like I had been ripped in half (which, arguably, I had been).

The community we were living in was wonderful. I returned home from the hospital to a sparkling-clean house, big happy signs on the door, and meals for two weeks. A wonderful friend kept me supplied with frozen soups, so between that and the daily meal that was sent by members of the community, we had two prepared meals every day.

After I got home from the hospital, though, things were in a bit of a panic. My husband took off work during the day, but was still working evenings, so I was on my own for dinner/bedtime. I hired a few girls to come help me – not a single one lasted more than half an hour before bringing my children back home for me to deal with. It was hard, and I'm not a complainer.

Looking back, I have no idea what happened because everything is in a haze. I was so tired, I let my girls sleep as long as they wanted when I should have been waking them every three hours to feed. This resulted in my girls losing weight, so every day was nurse, pump, nurse, pump. I nursed twelve times per day and pumped six. Nothing was helping, and I was feeling like a failure, trying to survive on two hours of sleep a night and unable to feed my babies. In addition, we were in limbo. We were packing to move because we had to leave our apartment two weeks after the babies were born.

Thank God I healed quickly. My husband had taken off of work (mostly) for the summer, so he was able to deal with the older boys while I concentrated on the twin girls. I feel that if we had had a bit more support from family who could help take care of the older boys, my husband would have been able to help me more with the girls, and I would have been able to take a bit more time to recover and focus on learning how to nurse two babies. As it was, I was back on my feet a week postpartum doing preschool pickup, driving my girls to the hospital for hearing tests, and other such necessary activities. And I had difficulties finding a lactation consultant to come help me figure out why my girls were not gaining weight and my milk supply wasn't increasing to meet their needs.

I'm sorry to say I don't remember much of the first few weeks and months after their birth. Some things are so clear, like my fury at the doctors for failing to recognize that my baby B had stopped growing in utero, causing her to have a few health issues at birth, and my frustration over their lack of weight gain and how strongly I rallied against supplementing with formula. There were issues with them not sleeping - I am a big believer in co-sleeping but I just couldn't do it with both of them. Other things are hazy, like what I ate on a daily basis, if I ate at all. I wore them in a baby carrier when they were fussy and had one baby swing that they spent a lot of time in. So I can't remember if they cried a lot. They did eat all the time, but it was always a struggle to nurse because I had to sit and use both hands instead of nursing on the go or in the carrier. I'm sure that my other three children were horribly neglected by me, but thankfully they don't seem to remember that, and had their wonderful father to compensate (even though it meant I had to do baby duty all on my own, full-time).

They're ten months old now. They are mostly breastfed, with formula to supplement and three full meals a day. They are a whole new experience from my three previous children. I'm still struggling to come to terms with their birth, those difficult first months of their lives, and my difficulties breastfeeding. They are beautiful, happy, energetic, and still don't sleep at night – hah!

Looking back, there were many things I should have, could have, and would have done differently. But there are things I cannot change, and I must accept that as it is.

Born Perfect

He was here at last, after many long months of worries, frightening tests, and determined reading of the medical literature.

Jen S.
Mom, English literature instructor, editor
Age 40
Second of two births

With the help of my doula, my son was cozily nursing, carefully swaddled and snuggled against me on the delivery bed. The sounds and excitement around us receded, and even the pain of the afterbirth, being coaxed out from somewhere beyond me, hardly registered. He was here at last, after many long months of worries, frightening tests, and determined reading of the medical literature. And he was absolutely perfect. The soft little gums seeking the first drops of colostrum proved it. Hazily, I watched my husband slip his finger into the baby's tiny mouth just after his first cry and sigh in relief. No, the cleft didn't extend to the palate, which we had not been able to determine conclusively by ultrasound.

I heard the midwife fussing at my husband, who hung over the scales with his camera, that maybe I wouldn't want him to be taking photos. But why not? The reason I felt it so important to take photos of Seth was that I had read online on one of the cleft sites about a man in his twenties describing how there were no photographs of him as a baby, and he had felt that his parents must have thought he had looked monstrous if they hadn't taken photos. We had discussed this beforehand and had made a decision to make sure to take photos of Seth in the delivery room.

Anyway, our baby had at last arrived and I knew he would be all right when, unlike most cleft babies, he started to nurse just like his big sister before him. I never gave her a bottle, and his sucking brought back to me that warm bond we had created during her nursing years. It felt right to photograph these initial moments. Too soon they took him away, so that the pediatrician could decide if he indeed should be nursing. If there was one thing I was determined to do, it was to nurse my cleft-lip son, so when the pediatrician came back affirming nursing was "OK'd," I was relieved I wouldn't have to push the issue with hospital staff.

I chose rooming in when we moved up to the ward, so he could nurse when he wanted, and anyhow, after waiting so long for him, why would I want to give him up? He was so perfect. He looked just like the reassuring photos of the cleft babies we had endlessly viewed online after the diagnosis in the second trimester by our private ultrasound specialist – my compromise for not doing amniocentesis after age thirty-five. He had tremendous, almost black eyes. He nursed regularly and slept peacefully, and it was so quiet and calm with him nearby.

But on the second day, the monitor clipped to his toe indicated he wasn't breathing properly while nursing, and they whisked him away to the preemie ward at the far end of the corridor that was lit all night and punctuated by the sounds of alarms and machines. He wasn't a preemie, but the staff reasoned he needed similar care. He would be cumbersomely attached to a more sophisticated monitor while I nursed him, all the while supplemented with formula. The room was filled with tiny, sick babies connected to numerous machines and hovered over by medical staff, who, although warm and helpful, weren't family, and certainly weren't the mother.

I needed to wake myself up throughout the night to use the

nursing pump, in the room next to the preemies, in order to establish my milk supply properly. It felt cold and dark in the halls, and I was so tired. He could still nurse, but the milk I pumped went into little bottles in the fridge that were measured and delivered in his Haberman Feeder, a special bottle for cleft babies. The only reward was watching the sun rise brilliantly and overwhelmingly red over the hills and valleys in the cold morning beneath the preemie ward, as I nursed him on a rocking chair, taking care to not dislodge his monitor.

Although his breathing seemed to be OK once he was under the preemie ward care, the staff then started worrying that I wasn't producing enough milk. He needed to be held in just the right position that would cover up the cleft to produce a vacuum, and the nursing pump was meant to stimulate milk production in case he was latching on too weakly. But the milk comes in slowly for a few days anyway, I thought to myself, and once he had been put on a more stable monitor in the preemie unit, there were no further problems with his respiration. So why were they so concerned?

The older children came to visit, and his four-year-old sister asked where the hole was in his face that we had told her about before he was born. He was so cute, who would notice? (Later on, I took Seth to his older sister's kindergarten, and was incredibly upset when the teacher told me not to take him into the classroom with his face uncovered because it might scare the children. Children are just curious, and when you explain it to them, they don't mind at all.)

The doctors told me we would need to stay in the hospital longer than usual, just to make sure he was OK and I would manage to feed him. I cried.

On the fifth day, they let us go home. He was gaining weight, and the doctor decided he could go back to exclusive nursing. He did not cry much, but when he did cry, nursing calmed him right away. He nursed every two to three hours during the day, and more often at night, but he slept right at the foot of my bed so it was not disturbing in the way it had been when he was in the preemie ward. After so many months of anxiety while we awaited his arrival, all was going well.

At his four-week checkup, he had only gained two hundred grams (seven ounces) since his birth weight. How had I not noticed? I had to go to a lactation consultant, and out came the formula and the Haberman Feeder again. I borrowed a nursing pump and pumped after every feeding to stimulate milk production. In addition to dealing with the pump, and the little bottles of breast milk, I had to fasten a complicated system of bandages to his face for the orthodontic procedure that was preparing him for his cleft surgery, and he wore a plastic plate in his mouth to cover an opening between his gum and his nose.

The pump was running frequently, its white noise filling our bedroom. I took its rhythmic humming to mean: "Leave him alone, leave him alone..." I had this subconscious sense that he was being given too much intervention.

That having been said, as my lactation consultant pointed out, the pumping WAS necessary because he couldn't create enough of a vacuum to produce adequate milk, and the pumping brought my milk supply up to a suitable level for him. Thankfully, this made it pretty easy after the surgery for him to just take up exclusive nursing.

At five weeks postpartum, I was secluded to bed with pneumonia because otherwise the doctors said they would need to hospitalize me. In actuality, this order was a relief. Between the nursing and the pumping and the bottle-feeding, there wasn't much time left anyway. We also had three other children who needed to eat dinner, and two weeks after he was born I had returned to teaching two classes, one afternoon a week, because I wasn't able to claim maternity leave. (He came with me to the teacher's college where I taught, and waited in the hallway with my parents so that he could nurse between sessions.) What a pleasure it was to just stay in bed, even if I did have pneumonia.

His surgery was to take place at four months of age, shortly after I would finish teaching for the semester. During the lead-up to the surgery, I researched nursing after cleft surgeries. Since using a bottle was not allowed immediately after the surgery, most babies needed to be fed by syringe or other similar non-sucking method. But nursing was not generally considered a problem, and our surgeon was supportive of the idea. Still, there was the issue of the supplemental feeding. I read that supplemental feeding units might be of help, so I experimented with two different setups that delivered the formula or breast milk through a thin tube taped to the breast at the same time he was nursing. This worked, with a great deal of practice, so I switched to this in the days leading up to the surgery, and also stored up extra breast milk in freezer bags so that I could provide him exclusively with breast milk. I liked the idea that the stitches on his mouth would only come in contact with pure mother's milk.

He had been perfect from the first moment I had seen him in the delivery room, but after his surgery, in the recovery room, I saw his face was also whole now in a way that would make his life easier for him.

The nursing staff were nervous because they had never had a nursing cleft baby before, but the doctor said go ahead, and right away he latched on, forming a powerful vacuum he had never achieved before. When he had finished the bags of frozen milk, a friend pointed out to me that milk production usually responds to the changing demands of the baby. This made sense to me, and is one of the advantages of nursing – that you worry less about how much a baby drinks because you don't measure it in a bottle but simply respond to the baby's hunger. So despite my lactation consultant's concerns about my milk supply, I stopped pumping, and he continued to gain weight during the next few months while nursing exclusively. What was more was that he loved nursing so much that it was several years before he stopped. What a perfect child.

Healing

I took the portable phone into the shower and sobbed into it, screaming at my husband with a razor in hand.

JILL Z.
MOM
AGE 36
FOURTH OF FIVE BIRTHS

I repeatedly go through my story – the events before and after birth – that led up to my postpartum depression (PPD). Was it the miscarriage and consequent D&C surgery, followed by a quick conception shortly after? Was it the horrible, suffering physical pain I experienced throughout the majority of the pregnancy? Or maybe all the fear I experienced all day and night those long nine months that the pregnancy might not reach full term, might not give me a live baby, or a healthy baby. Who knows…

I conceived baby number four in the late fall. We had moved to a new city a bit over a year beforehand, and anyway we were anxious to have our next child. Yet I was still acclimating to our life in the new place, and all the small differences that add up to the big changes we all experienced upon settling here. The pregnancy was in the normal range for me up until four months. First it was the varicose veins in my thighs and legs – I began wearing the bulletproof stockings to contain the increasingly painful pressure. I couldn't stand in one place for long, nor wait in lines, nor cook. I always had to keep moving.

At about five months pregnant, I started to experience the symptoms of symphysis pubis dysfunction (SPD). SPD is caused by the hormonal changes during pregnancy. My pelvis was spreading wider and faster than the average pregnancy, which led to the worst pain I'd ever experienced in my life. It began with soreness in my inner thighs, then slowly became a near-debilitating constant pain. I felt as if someone had taken a hammer to my pelvic area. I didn't feel like anything was holding me together. I felt loose and wobbly. I couldn't walk up stairs, step into my stockings (nor any clothing, for that matter), get on and off the toilet, roll over in bed at night, or sleep without the perfect pillow between my thighs AND calves, or have relations with my husband, without terrible, excruciating pain. It developed to a point that I couldn't even cry anymore.

I went to my ob-gyn, who had such a great reputation, only to be told it was nothing. I didn't know if I was being dramatic, but it's not like me to complain. I usually can tough through most discomforts. By my ninth month, I'd been going to bed with my hands in fists and waking with them still balled up. I carried so much tension, and I felt very alone in my pain. I didn't know if I'd be able to birth my baby naturally, as I had hoped. What if my pelvic situation interfered with my birth? I couldn't imagine even spreading my legs to allow baby out. Every move hurt deeply.

I'd noticed I had fallen into a very internal state, which is normal pre-labor and delivery, but I was like that for over a month before my due date. At that time, I was so sick of all my negativity and fear, I didn't want to hear myself speak to anyone. My husband was consumed by the new business he was starting, and I didn't have a strong enough support system to pull me out of the place I was already in.

All I wanted was to have a healthy baby and not be pregnant anymore. I counted down those days in hours, and my due date, for the first time ever, went by with no labor – no signs of anything. I was so desperate that at nine days post-due, I drank my neighbor's breast milk mixed with raw eggs and honey – a sure concoction to push me over – and it worked.

I used the HypnoBirthing method for the first time, and the baby came much faster than I expected. Before I even left for the hospital, I went into transition and felt my baby crowning. My husband was downstairs organizing last-minute details. It all happened so fast, my doula made it when baby began to officially crown. The ambulance arrived shortly after and a medic caught my new baby girl. In other words, this was an unplanned homebirth.

The aftermath was uneventful. I was elated to have been given the gift of a healthy baby. Upon returning home from the hospital, I was desperate to exclusively nurse this baby. I had been unsuccessful in the past. I gave it my all that first month. I went on barely any sleep as my baby cried and cried. I went to the best lactation consultant around. She told me after all of our hard work that my baby wasn't gaining weight and I had to supplement with formula. I was devastated. And I was in a space of such sleep deprivation that I was on my way downhill. The endorphins from birth now faded, and the reality that my new baby still cried a majority of the day even on formula was throwing me over the edge. I was drained on all levels.

At about six weeks postpartum, I remember my brother-in-law visiting. I was preparing some food in the kitchen, and I clearly remember the moment I became aware that my thoughts were very dark and negative. Very unlike me. I turned to my husband and started sobbing in his arms, repeating, "Something is wrong with me, something is not right in my head." I was given hugs and love but nothing beyond. And the truth is, I didn't know I was continuing on a downward spiral. I was very weepy, not wanting to talk to anyone.

In December, four months after birth, we went on a ski trip. I remember leaving my baby for hours with the babysitter, just happy to be free of the responsibility. I was still in a negative headspace, becoming more detached from the baby and feeling a lot of anger at the rest of my children and my husband.

We returned from the ski trip to move houses. The change of environment sent me even more over the edge. I'm not sure when or how, but around five months postpartum, I'd hit bottom. I'd already detached from my baby – I'd leave her with the sitter and not even say bye, nor acknowledge her upon my return.

I desperately tried to exercise to increase my endorphin levels and lose my weight, but it didn't help me. I'd seen my ob-gyn at three months for a routine checkup, and when she asked how I was, I began to cry. Once again she failed me, saying only that I'm always such a happy person and "It will pass, the crying." She'd fit me for a Mirena (hormonal) IUD for birth control. I asked if perhaps the hormonal birth control would affect my moods, and she said no, it was too localized to affect my head.

But I was stuck in my head, stuck in my thoughts. I never wanted to harm the baby, but I didn't feel much toward her and I definitely didn't want to care for her. My most vivid memory was crying hysterically on the phone to my husband that I didn't want to live this life. I spoke of running away, leaving my husband and children, killing myself. I actually took the portable phone into the shower and sobbed into it screaming at my husband with a razor in hand threatening to kill myself. My husband was too consumed to really see what I was going through, and he had no awareness that I could actually be mentally ill. He did, however, call my mother, who grabbed the next flight out to see me.

The moment my mother saw me, she knew I was GONE. In my mind I was angry – normally I do love my mother and would've been excited to see her, even if it was unannounced, but when she walked up those stairs, I was enraged and didn't want to see her nor speak to her. I felt rage at my husband for secretly flying her out to check up on me. At times I knew something was wrong with me, but I was still too proud to accept that I might need help.

In the end, my mother confirmed that I was not all there. My husband helped get me to a postpartum depression support organization, which ultimately saved me.

Alternative therapies did not help me. I needed to go on an antidepressant, which kicked in three weeks later. I also changed from the Mirena to a non-hormonal birth control - instinctively I didn't listen to the doctor because I felt that the Mirena largely affected my moods. In a snap, I was back! What a miracle. I stayed on the medication for the recommended six months and then reevaluated. Once I was balanced medically, I found that I could keep my emotional balance by regular exercise. I started waking up at 5 A.M. and would go running with a friend most mornings, arriving back home just before the children woke up. That gave me physical relief and a feeling that I had my own time to take care of myself.

I'm very grateful that the PPD did not continue on any longer, and I was able to seek help. The most mystifying part was how no one picked up on my suffering. I was in such a dark, alone place and too proud to open up to anyone, yet nobody, even my own husband, saw any red flashing lights to see that I needed help. And the antidepressant medication was supposed to be "hush-hush" because there's a shame in taking it. I'm not saying this because I'm upset about it. I'm mentioning it because there needs to be an increased awareness and a level of comfort and openness for women to say "I'm not OK" without feeling like a failure.

One way I healed was with my next pregnancy. I was highly fearful of getting pregnant again, and of having all that pain, and of postpartum depression reoccurring. We were also not in a financial situation where we could afford another baby. But I prayed that my husband would get a different job, and then I'd do my own emotional and spiritual work to be ready for a baby. And that's what happened. I went to a counselor who guided me on how to view my last experience as a growth opportunity. If God already gave me that experience, I could trust that I wouldn't have to have it again. I spoke with God and worked on my relationship with Him, and this process also helped me in my relationship with my husband. I worked on thought control to have only positive thoughts.

Thankfully, my pregnancy was incredibly healthy with only minor aches. And when I started to feel twinges of that "cloud of darkness" in the late third trimester, I got a prescription for the antidepressant Zoloft, just in case I'd need it postpartum. I nursed my baby for two weeks, but then felt I needed the meds, so that was my priority. I went with my instincts and had a good postpartum period this time. While I would never wish the experience of PPD on anyone, for me in the end it necessitated a lot of effective, positive changes in my life, and for that I'm grateful.

The effects my PPD had on my daughter seem long-lasting. She's over five years old now, and is constantly asking for attention for mild aches ("boo-boos"), not just from me but from almost anyone, including her teachers, many times during the day. It used to be cute but it's gotten out of hand.

I consulted with another mother whom I look up to, and she advised me to not blow it off. She said that perhaps this is my daughter's wounded soul from my not being able to be there for her emotionally at the beginning of her life. So I can heal it now. She suggested I be fully present for any complaint about a boo-boo. To stop everything, get down to my daughter's height and look her in the eye and ask her, "Are you OK? Would you like me to make an appointment with the doctor? Because I will! I'll call him right now!" And to not fake it. To really mean it. To let her know I'm there for her. And wouldn't you know it? Her complaints are lessening. She'll say, "Mommy – I'm OK! It's OK!" I feel really relieved knowing I can heal my daughter's leftover emotional pain, years later. This, in turn, heals me too.

Losing My Second

I wanted to take her home. Prop her up in her highchair. Maybe through the sheer power of my wishes to mother her, to raise her, to love her, I could will her alive.

ABBIE G.
MOM
AGE 38
SECOND OF SEVEN BIRTHS

Should I hold my dead baby?

I was nine months pregnant, on the labor and delivery floor, waiting for the contractions to kick in. Pushing out my first baby, a live girl, had been a physical challenge, to say the least. Knowing I had to do this again, for a dead baby, "for nothing," caused desperation. Having a baby is "good pain," my sister-in-law, who had endured so much "bad pain" in her losing battle with cancer, had once told me. Birthing a dead baby, if you can call it birthing – that's bad pain, right? I would have confirmed with her if I could.

Only when my baby was dead, still floating in my body, did I understand how thoughtful I had been for nine months about the food I ate, the naps I caught, the plans I made. Everything I had done had been with this little life in mind. With a rush of intensity I now saw that sleep as wasted time, those nauseous mornings as pointless torture, the pounds gained as foolish.

Worst of all, my future months were empty. My plans had been my baby.

There were hours between the frozen moment when the ultrasound screen displayed (for reasons that were and remain unknown) an utterly lifeless baby and the time my body was ready to expel it. The social workers and nurses who visited me during that time told me that holding and talking to the baby was recommended. I was terrified by the idea. What would it look like? I had never touched a dead body before or even seen one. Hold the baby? Talk to it? Not for me. But as the hours passed, my husband Mark and I talked.

By the middle of the night, when the time for the actual delivery came, I had succumbed to the advice to hold my baby, a girl, like I had with my first child. She looked a lot like her big sister. And not scary at all. She looked like a sleeping baby. My problem stopped being fear of holding her. Instead I did not want to give her up. I wanted to keep talking to this beautiful baby who could have been simply sleeping in my arms. I wanted to dress her. I wanted to take her home. Prop her up in her highchair. Maybe through the sheer power of my wishes to mother her, to raise her, to love her, I could will her alive.

Now that I had been convinced to hold her, when was I supposed to let go of her and say goodbye to her precious, perfect baby body? "You make me hold her and then I'm supposed to give her up?" I wanted to say to the now-absent social worker. I was scared and sad and felt like I was betraying her when they took her out of the room for the last time. But before they took her body from me forever, they dressed her and photographed her. They took more than one photo. Why more than one? It was not like she messed up the picture by moving or blinking.

They hung a special sign on the door so that the new shift of workers at the hospital would know my baby was dead and hopefully not say the wrong thing when they entered to take my blood pressure or take out the garbage.

Mark and I, in our grief, mine already much deeper than his, did feel sincere gratitude that I was still healthy and fine, though we would soon find out that "fine" can mean really sad. And anxious.

The hospital released me as quickly as possible. Apparently, getting a sad women with a dead baby away from the halls of the maternity ward and their exhausted but hope-imbued aura, for her own sake, outweighs the need to continue to monitor her pulse, temperature, and blood pressure at all hours of the day and night. The doctor even said that if it would help me feel better, I could take baths and swim fairly soon, which otherwise would have been forbidden for weeks.

I arrived home right before the weekend. Though so many people had offered to help us, stupidly we took no help. I remember calling a local takeout store on Friday morning, to order food for the weekend. He told me that he was sorry but they only took orders until Thursday. I told him I knew that, and that I had just had a dead baby and I couldn't stop crying and he said he was sorry and he delivered food to us.

Over the weekend, in my head, I drafted the message I would send to all of our friends. I told them we were sad, but able to laugh. We were thankful for each other and our wonderful living daughter. I told them they could just say they were sorry, or they could say more, but that they should say something. I still have the wonderfully kind messages we received in return, right away, and for many days and weeks and months.

Everywhere I went for the next few weeks, I felt an overwhelming need to send the message of my dead baby there first. I did not want to go anywhere and see anyone who might mistakenly congratulate me. Not the kind, grandfatherly, and long-married-yet-childless doorman in my building whose suffering surely surpassed mine, not the lifeguards where I had swum regularly for the health of my pregnant body and my growing baby - not anyone, anywhere. I sent my husband into our building first to tell the doorman, and asked him to tell the neighbors. One day

I frantically ran down one escalator and up another in a crowded Barnes & Noble in midtown Manhattan so I could catch up with the lifeguard at the pool where I swam, whom I spotted amidst the crowd. I felt unglued as I tried to control a situation long out of my hands, asking this lifeguard to tell all the other people at the pool what had happened so that they would not dare wish me – the mom of only a dead baby – "congratulations" when they saw me back again, with my postpartum body so exposed.

Two or three weeks later, I invited two lovely couples – friends – for lunch. Both had newborn baby girls. They both said they were surprised to get the invitation but understood that having them and their babies over must somehow have been important to me. I do recall being genuinely happy to see their babies and enjoying our time together. It was only later that seeing any babies or toddlers the age of my now-buried daughter caused me to avert my glance. Those lovely, innocent, living girls are invisible to me. I don't remember their names, and I have consciously lost touch with all but the most persistent parents of children born alive between my oldest daughter and my second living daughter.

I had no desire to harm myself or anyone else. But for months I was sad. I felt depressed, and that's a scary word and a terrible feeling. I went to a therapist, almost hoping she could give me something for my pain. All she could tell me was that what had happened to me was traumatic. And depressing. My feelings were normal.

Rebirthing

I stroked his small body and wondered at his impossibly small fingers and toes. I looked at him and gave him the respect he deserved as our son.

BETH S.
MOM, FOUNDER OF SPECIAL-NEEDS/MAINSTREAM CHILDREN'S DAY CAMP
AGE 45
THIRD OF THREE BIRTHS

I can see myself. Walking back and forth in the parlor. All night. Trying to relax, breathe, and go with the program. I can't. We walk downstairs. I need help. Somehow the act of walking downstairs, while in the transition stage of labor, is the scariest thing I've ever done in my life. More than the birth that still awaits – I haven't thought that far.

We're in our bedroom. Looking for a comfortable position. I've been pushing for some time. I'm tired. There's a part of me that worries whether I can do this. Have a VBAC as planned. As dreamed, as imagined, as wanted so badly, more than anything I've wanted ever. I'll be devastated if I get transferred to the hospital. My midwife is calm. My husband is calm. The doula is calm. Only I'm not sure.

Every birth is an adventure. A live event, a testimony of what we hope for, what we wish for, and the reality of the experience.

Nine months you've waited patiently. Even with prenatal testing and having a confirmation of gender, there are still questions to be answered by the final appearance of the long-awaited infant.

Labor. Now there's a word to breed fear into the average woman. I wondered, along with my friends, how I'd do, how we'd all do during our individual birth adventures. We repeated war stories heard from women who'd come before us, along with the stories of transcending pain and finding that place of empowerment in birth. I was unsure. What kind of laboring mother-to-be would I be?

That first time, secure in my naïveté, I assumed I'd have the perfect "natural" birth, whatever that meant. Sure, I wanted a healthy baby and all, but I also yearned for some sort of female-specific experience, something that would make me "feel like a woman," united with so many predecessors.

My mother was limited in her birth stories, speaking of a difficult unmedicated birth for my brother, her first. He was breech, and in those pre-malpractice-we'll-just-section-you days, she gave birth vaginally. Imagine that. The next three, which included me, were blissfully "under the influence."

"They put me to sleep and when I woke up I had a new baby," she described, secure in her belief that her way was the best way to give birth. I disagreed. After all, this was 1990. I assumed that I'd give birth without medication, with my obstetrician's complete support of my birth plan. I would be in charge of my birth. Boy, was I wrong.

Forty hours after my water broke, as my labor piddled along and my temperature rose, as the shifts changed and the doctor walked in and out without much to offer, I gave up and agreed to a C-section. Our eldest, now twenty-three, was born – healthy and whole. I felt robbed. I talked endlessly about my story, attending a support group with other couples who'd had birth experiences that made them question and grieve. Almost two years later, after reading, weeping, and railing my way through a succession of excellent books about birth in the twentieth century (my favorite was Suzanne Arms's *Immaculate Deception*), I became pregnant again.

I prepared my head. No more meditative chapters on visual imagery and effective labor, rhythmic breathing and the best music playlist to prepare. I read stories of the angry and the triumphant, the still-in-pain and the healed. My husband even found a book – *The Vaginal Birth After Cesarean (VBAC) Experience: Birth Stories by Parents and Professionals* – that moved him, one that responded to the spouse's experience. He'd been disappointed too, of course.

That second birth, in our home, was far from easy but it was triumphant. I'd done it. We'd done it. Our team of midwife, doula, and my younger sister (who was in charge of our eldest during the birth) supported and believed in us. Our second son nursed well from the start, something that had initially defeated me that first time, given that my baby was stowed away in the NICU on a different floor from me. Why do they take the baby away from the mother, and for so long?

And yet, the miracle that awaited me was my third birth, four years later. It was the birth that was most fully realized, if that makes sense, the one where I put it all together and just let it happen. Too bad we never had a fourth – I always wondered how another birth might have been.

That first week, as we navigated visits to the pediatrician and then the neonatologist, followed by the cardiologist, as I attempted to nurse my newest who just wasn't latching on as I'd have liked, as we reveled in the ease of his birth, we staggered in the shock of his diagnosis. Going into nursing overdrive, the threat of hospitalization over my head if he didn't start gaining weight, the success of the birth retreated, overwhelmed as we were by what we didn't know. About disability. About Down syndrome. About this new parenting adventure upon which we were embarking.

One part of me recognized that I was ready. That we were

ready. I was a mature and capable mother. He was, at the end of the day, a baby. I knew babies. I was a stay-at-home parent, homeschooling our young family in an enriching and exciting urban community with much to offer. Surely, he would fit right in to our child-led parenting and way of living. The other part of me wasn't sure what to think. I had little experience with children with any kinds of disabilities except for one family in our community whom we respected and admired... from afar. As for Down syndrome and developmental delay, what would that really mean, we wondered.

We grieved for what we thought might never happen: his wedding (probably not), graduation ceremony (it was great), communicating (yup, in his own way), living independently (not likely, but we're OK with that). It all seemed very big. And it was, but then we remembered, he's just an infant. Why not start at the beginning and let him show us his own path, his own likes and loves, his special talents and his challenges?

A month later, the baby still wasn't able to breastfeed, and I wanted to do something different to spur on more bonding with him. So, upon the suggestion of my lactation consultant, he and and I took a special bath together. We remembered the birth – at least I did. I thought about the meaning of the birth for me, the sense of renewed victory at doing it the way I wanted, the way we had planned, and the way it felt best for us as a family. As I sat in the cooling bath water, holding the baby – he always seemed in those early days "not quite ready for prime time" – I reclaimed my right, our right, to his birth and his right to be part of our family despite the confusion and fear of those early weeks of his life. This, during a period where people often asked, and continued to ask, if we had tested, and if we had known before he was born. As if we needed more reasons to doubt our choices.

And I knew, on a deeper level – if not then, then in the following year or so – that I was unlikely to birth again. I come from a family of four kids, my husband from two. Three was a good number for us. Now with these special circumstances –

and we really had no idea what lay before us – from epilepsy to significant developmental issues to his diagnosis with autism spectrum disorder later in childhood, this beautiful baby was to be my last pregnancy and birth. I was grateful to have "gotten it right." At least the birth was right, I reasoned with myself, if not quite the baby – an honest but uncomfortable thought I didn't like to consider.

And yet I was grateful. We were grateful for this third addition to our young family. Read the well-known essay by Emily Perl Kingsley titled "Welcome to Holland" for a better explanation of the feelings a family experiences when a child is born different. In essence, you've packed for Italy and discover you're in Holland. But, there are tulips... it's nice in Holland.

When my lactation consultant initially suggested this "rebirthing ceremony," it seemed almost hokey to me, but I knew I needed a way to recapture the joy, the gratitude, and the exhilaration of his arrival only four weeks earlier. She didn't give any real instructions. She just suggested that I go back to that moment before the water broke, before he emerged – he was almost born in his bag of waters, something the midwife said was considered great luck in certain societies – whole and present. I stroked his small body and wondered at his impossibly small fingers and toes. I looked at him and gave him the respect he deserved, the respect that he would always deserve as my son, as our son. Together, we rebirthed each other. And it was good.

Already Responsible

Girls my age want to have fun, go out, and just "be free." I stay home most of the time with my baby…

Natalie K.
Mom and student
Age 16
First birth

Pregnancy brought many challenges for me, aside from the nausea. I became pregnant when I was fifteen. For the first trimester, I was still going to high school, but I would throw up every day when I transferred buses on my way there. I had to drop out of school when my belly started to swell with new life. I lost friends when I left school. I had to disappear from the radar while my family and I readjusted to our new reality and worked out what our future would be like. I couldn't stay in touch with everyone for fear of people finding out about my pregnancy before I was ready to announce it. Although I had many challenges, one thing was for sure: my parents decided they would support me and help me and do everything they could to make me and my new baby feel loved and cared for.

A week before my due date, we moved to a different neighborhood – a more open-minded area, where we felt our situation would feel more comfortable. My mother told me she "didn't let" me give birth till after we had moved! I was a good girl and listened!

Finally, at week 41, I went into labor at 8 P.M. I had regular contractions for a few hours. A midwife friend came over, and I had my mother, who's a childbirth educator, with me too. I was very calm and relaxed and spent most of the labor in the bathtub and shower. At around midnight, we decided to head to the hospital after I felt a need to push! We got to the hospital at 1 A.M., and twenty minutes later I gave birth to a beautiful, healthy baby boy! Of course, seeing as the labor had gone so smoothly, that baby just HAD to do something special at the end – he came out with his hand on his head. I tore.

The most amazing thing was just holding him close to me and looking at him. Then, the hospital midwife said I needed stitches. I didn't even feel anything when I tore and at that time it really didn't bother me.

I couldn't sleep the whole night! I was so excited! (Plus, the lady next to me was snoring really loudly and kept mumbling things…) At 8:00 A.M. the next morning, my mother (who stayed with me overnight) and I called family and close friends to tell them that I had a baby, and everyone was very excited.

But the weekend was coming and there was no way I was going to stay in the hospital without all of my family! Luckily my mother knew exactly who to speak to, and at 10 A.M., we got permission to leave. I was so excited to go home and show off my little prince to everyone!

Being home was fun. My little sisters couldn't stop staring at him even though all he did was sleep. It was a little annoying going to the bathroom and having to wash off every time because I had stitches. The bleeding was fine, I didn't pay much attention to it, and everything else was great. Only until it was time to go to sleep…I was exhausted and just wanted to sleep, but baby had his own plans. Baby kept waking up every hour or so wanting to eat or just to be held! I was so tired and needed to sleep!! Very emotional and exhausted, I walked into my mother's bedroom with the baby and just started crying! I felt like it was just too much for me! My mother took the baby and told me to lie down on her bed. I immediately fell asleep, and she put the baby next to me and spoke to him. When he wanted to eat again, my mother showed me how to nurse lying down.

In the morning, I only ate a little bit. I had no appetite and my stomach was achy. But I slept a lot. Every time that baby fell asleep, I quickly jumped into bed!

It all felt very special having my sisters around to get me anything I needed, having my mother around to help me emotionally and with the baby, and also having my father there helping, too! It was nice and a lot easier living at home with my baby, getting the kind of help that maybe our foremothers got when they gave birth surrounded by family - especially female family members.

I didn't know when my milk was going to come in and THAT was a nice surprise! The next morning, I woke up soaking wet!! It was funny!

On day 4 after the birth, I still had some pain... like very light contractions. My mother told me it was my womb getting small again. It wasn't very painful, it was just very uncomfortable! By now, my appetite came back. So I was able to eat some cake at my sister's birthday party! (Although I only took one bite and baby started crying for me.)

For some reason, I didn't want anyone to hold the baby, only me and my parents.

That night, baby got his first bath. My mother bathed him and I took pictures - I still felt tired and a little weak. That same night, baby woke up only twice to eat! He slept most of the night, and I think it was because we gave him a bath right before he went to sleep.

On day 5, after everyone kept asking to hold him, I let them, and I was fine with it. Then later I was in a quiet room nursing the baby, and I suddenly started crying. My mother came in and asked me why I was crying but I didn't have an answer. I just let myself cry. It felt good.

By now, everything was getting much better. I was eating a lot (because I was nursing...), I didn't have any pain anymore, and the bleeding was just like a normal period, not heavy like at the beginning.

When my baby was about a month old, I started going out again, just for fresh air, and it really helped me since I needed it, and it was good for baby, too!

I always tried to be as calm as possible, not only around the baby, but especially around him. Sometimes it was hard when I would change his diaper and just when I'd close his last button, he would poo again. So I would stay calm and say, "Well, at least he waited until I closed the diaper so he didn't poo all over me." It also helps that babies are so cute! You just can't get too upset...

I got the most help from my parents. They basically helped me with everything! From the first day of the pregnancy until today, they are my heroes!

I love breastfeeding, and I'm not planning on stopping for a long time. And when baby just stares into your eyes and you just melt away...love.

A few weeks later, I started thinking about going back to school, and then again, about exercising. I went running a few times and it was just so hard! I was always out of breath, and I gave up.

Living at home with my sisters around could be a lot of fun and very helpful. But there are times when it's not easy with them. The baby is still new to them, and they're not used to having a baby around. So when it's baby's bedtime, it's hard for them to remember that there is a baby sleeping in their house, and I have to go upstairs to him a few times when he gets woken up, and put him back to sleep. Hopefully soon he will get used to the noise and will be able to sleep through their loud talk and loud singing!

Thank God, I didn't get the "baby blues." I got help from my family and friends, so I never felt depressed. But I did cry sometimes when I was too tired to deal with the baby, and so then I got help and I would take a nap or something. I also tried to avoid getting depressed by singing a lot. I would always sing and talk to my baby, and when he smiled back, I couldn't be depressed even if I wanted to! I think that if I had gotten depressed, it would have been because I am a single mom, I am fully responsible for my baby, I don't have a husband to help me in the middle of the night when I'm tired and baby starts crying. Also, for my age, it's so much! Girls my age want to have fun, go out, and just "be free." I went back to high school, so when I'm not in class, I stay home most of the time with my baby. I have a life started already at such a young age and it can be so hard! Sometimes I do cry, I just cry it out and it passes. I think I'm doing a good job.

Making It Happen

Choosing at the age of thirty-nine to become a single mother by choice did make me happy, but I learned very quickly that when a baby cries at 4 in the morning, no one else will take care of her.

LEAH L.
DOCTOR OF CHIROPRACTIC, PHOTOGRAPHER
AGE 46 (40 AT THE TIME OF THE BIRTH)
FIRST BIRTH

In my seventh month of pregnancy, I began to tell my clients that I would be taking maternity leave. Most of my patients expressed mild surprise, because at that point of my pregnancy I had gained no more than ten pounds; some commented that they thought I had "gained a little weight recently."

One older woman, who knew my family, responded less enthusiastically.

Me: Starting next month, I will be on maternity leave.

Woman: That's so nice of you, taking off time to help your older sister take care of her children.

Me: No, I am taking off time to take care of my baby.

Woman: You have a baby in there?

Me: I do! Do you want to see the ultrasound as proof of her existence?

Woman (shrugging a shoulder): Well, whatever makes you happy.

In fact, choosing at the age of thirty-nine to become a single mother by choice did make me happy, and I was enjoying every minute of the pregnancy. Every time I vomited during the first trimester, I would celebrate it, because it meant that the pregnancy was still working.

As I got closer to the due date, many of my friends said repeatedly, "You will not have to do this alone. We will be there to help you whenever you need us."

After the birth I learned very quickly that no matter how well-meaning the sentiment, in practice everyone leads their own busy lives, and when a baby cries at 4 in the morning, no one else will breastfeed her or change her diaper or rock her back to sleep. It is my job to take care of my daughter's physical and emotional health. I alone am responsible for the easy decisions (pink shirt or purple?) and the hard ones (caretakers and education). I can take all the credit, and twenty years from now on the therapist's couch, I will get all the blame.

When I went into labor, I called a cousin and asked him to put together the bassinet, feed the cat, and watch the house until I came home. He happily agreed. The day my daughter and I came home from the hospital, the living room had become a giant litter box. There was not a single sterile area in the apartment for a three-day-old girl. I spent two hours vacuuming and dusting and assembling furniture, leaving Rafaela on a small chair with pillows and praying that she would not yet learn how to roll over.

Before I was even allowed to leave the hospital, a social worker came to visit me in the maternity ward. She pulled a chair in front of me and whispered – the way people talk to someone ill with cancer – "I understand you are single mother. Do you have any friends or support system?" Having convinced the social worker that I had thought this through, she signed off on my chart. In fact, I had conducted two years of research and one year of intense work with a personal coach before beginning fertility treatments.

To drive a car you need to study and get a license. When I was studying the human body to become a doctor, I had to take four rounds of licensing exams. To make a baby, all you need are two adults and penetration, or in my case, hormones and a syringe. Later I wondered to myself why she only interviewed me in the ward that day, or if every couple is interrogated before they take home their precious bundle.

My parents flew in to meet my daughter. For the first day after they arrived, they helped me out - sort of. Luckily, I had arranged to have meals delivered from friends for the first week after I came home. But soon after, my dad discovered that my cable package included ESPN, and while I was in my bedroom collapsing from exhaustion and breastfeeding on demand, my parents were watching the Red Sox game.

You see, my daughter barely slept for the first year and a half, because she knew that there was a party somewhere, and she didn't want to miss out. When she did sleep, she was like a Swiss watch, waking up every morning at 5:30, and this genetic programming continues to this day. At the time, my body adapted to fewer than three hours of sleep per night.

When Rafaela was about four months old, there was one night that I could not settle her, no matter what I tried. Though she was normally not fussy or a crier, nothing soothed her that night, and I had reached the end of my physical and mental tolerance. For the first time in my life, I could understand the chain of events leading up to shaken baby syndrome, and didn't plan on going there. I quickly decided to put Rafaela into her bassinet and shut the door. Then I called a friend and neighbor, who immediately came over and stayed with her until she fell asleep, while I sat in the living room and cried.

I marveled every day at this gift of a child and accepted the trials that go along with being a new mother. Getting to know Rafaela's soul and watching her grow gave me joy that I could not have ever imagined, and as soon as she appeared on the scene, my whole adult single life felt like a distant memory, like a biographical documentary you watch about someone else.

I have stopped counting the number of times since Rafaela

was born six years ago that I hear, "Oh, you're so brave!" I do not consider myself brave in any way. I wanted to carry a child, experience pregnancy, and become a mother, rather than live with regret. These days, as I drive my daughter back and forth from school and lessons and doctor's appointments, I see myself not as a single mother but as Mommy, a busy multitasking woman like many of my friends, married or otherwise.

The most difficult part of single parenting is not, as one would imagine, the financial stress, being the sole provider for our small, untraditional family. When Rafaela makes me laugh, or performs a beautiful act of warmth and kindness, there is no one else on the planet who appreciates her as much as I do. And when I must make what feels like the most crucial decision in her life, I have no sound board or second opinion. No one asks me about my day, and the conversations about Queen Elsa and unicorns can make your head explode without some intelligent adult conversation or physical intimacy. Most days I am too tired to even think about reentering the dating scene, and I miss the era when I could go to the gym four or five times per week.

And yet, every night after Rafaela goes to sleep, I sneak into her room and watch her, and it takes my breath away: the softness of her face, the fullness of her lips, her mane of golden curls, and her contented smile. I am blessed to have this amazing child, this most beautiful continuation of my family's legacy, and I cannot imagine who I would be without her.

The Adoption Option

One of the hardest parts of this process was the not knowing when we would be matched with a baby. It's not like being pregnant – although I was "expecting," there was no growth to show for it.

Elisheba H.
Art educator
Age 46
First baby

When I was in my late thirties, single *again*, I decided that rather than waiting around for the "perfect" partner, I would begin the journey of motherhood. I figured that I knew so many families – mine included – that started with certain constellations that changed; in other words, some couples broke up and some single people found mates *after* their children were born. Pursuing a single-mother-by-choice route, I asked a few potential donors if they would consider helping me.

After some consideration, a gay friend told me that it is not his "karmic destiny to have biological progeny in this lifetime." Another potential donor suggested I try a sperm bank, which I eventually did, buying about six rounds of sperm.

Along the way, I met Bob.

After a month or so of dating, I decided to share with him my "project." He was slightly taken aback, sharing that this was not how he had imagined having a family, but it didn't end our relationship. Though I was not ready to have him father my child, I changed the sperm donor specs to match his appearance: blue eyes, curly brown hair, 5'7". (All of these physical details are on the menu of donor choices.) I did not conceive. When eventually Bob and I imagined really committing to raising children together, I still did not conceive. We became engaged and while in the process of planning our wedding, went to see a fertility specialist (we were, after all, in our late thirties already - in fact, thirty-nine at that point.)

The specialist charged us $200 for a forty-five-minute session, during which he showed us a PowerPoint presentation about his most-recommended procedure, artificial insemination. It included statistics based on our ages. Near the end of the appointment, I asked, "Do I understand this right? For $16,000 I can get hormone injections for several months and go through this painful and invasive process so that we will have a 20 percent chance of conceiving? And if we do conceive, there is a greater than 50 percent risk that we will have clubfooted, cleft palate, mongoloid twins?" He didn't laugh, but I did.

After leaving the specialist's office, I turned to Bob and said, "I am not attached to having a biological child - I want to be a mother. Let's adopt. With adoption, it's not an 'if,' it's a 'when,' for having a child." My mate was not as open to the idea. It took him a few months (and a few sessions with a therapist) to wrap his mind around this path to parenthood. But he came around, realizing he really did want to be a father.

We went to the adoption classes - the orientation, sessions with adoptive parents, adoptees, and even birth parents. In doing so, our preconceived notions were knocked down as we learned the truth about the process, the field, and some best practices for the psychological development of the adoptee.

Just what were these preconceived notions, you might wonder? Well, Bob's initial response to my declaration that I wanted to adopt was something like this: "I am happy as I am. I'm not interested in adoption. And I think those kids always have problems – wherever they go, everyone knows they are adopted." When explored further, what he was thinking was based on his sister's experiences as a social worker for children of different races than the parents who have adopted them.

I think we both went in thinking something like this: Women who put their children up for adoption are poor. They are probably drug addicts and/or alcoholics. I am ashamed to write this, as I don't really know where this notion comes from, but when I honestly look at what I imagined, this was one of the archetypes in my mind. The other experience I'd had was of babies adopted from China or Vietnam, or who are otherwise racially different from the adopting parents I know.

In both these cases, when the family walks down the street there may be people who look quizzical or judge them. My partner's concern was that these kids would always feel "other," or that they wouldn't truly belong.

But one thing we learned is that for many impoverished people who live, say, in inner cities and get pregnant while in high school, or don't have college degrees or careers, having a baby gives them purpose and direction. In many communities, grandmothers and aunties provide support for young women to bring babies into the world. Therefore, this is not necessarily a culture that supports putting babies up for adoption. So our imagined "pregnant woman" would likely not be a birth mother based on our stereotypes.

Many babies are put up for adoption in America by unmarried women who get pregnant but do not believe in abortion. Or by graduate students who are not at a point in their career paths to raise a baby, nor are they interested in aborting. Some birth moms, when they find out they are pregnant, want to carry to term so they can give the baby to a family that cannot give birth. And then – the biggest surprise – there are some families who already have kids and unexpectedly find themselves pregnant with another child who they are not ready to bring into the mix. This was really eye-opening.

When we first learned about international versus domestic adoption, we both immediately wanted to do domestic. The practice for about the past twenty years has been "open adoption," which means that both the birth mother and the adopting families have full access to information about each other. In fact, the birth mother usually *chooses* the adoptive family who will raise the baby. In some cases, the families have ongoing and open relationships with the birth mother. We wondered if it would be confusing to the child to have the birth mother around, but according to the research, a child cannot have too much love. At different developmental stages, the child has different needs and experiences, and what researchers found is that most kids - when given access to their birth parents and stories - just understand it as their story. They do not feel confused - they know who their parents are. When they have access, they can ask common questions such as, "Why did you put me up for adoption?" Or they can find out more about their biological health history.

We met one adopted adult who shared the story of growing up in a family where she looked physically very different. All her young life she yearned to find people she looked like. After years of searching, paying a private detective, and traveling across the country, she found her birth mother, only to be completely rejected by her. When she reflected on her process, she mused that if she had been given a photo, if she had just had one visual connection, it might have saved her much misery.

Another woman we met through the adoption process was a birth mother named Jenny. When her son was born, she chose a family to adopt him who lived within an hour of where she lived. The adopting family already had a daughter they had adopted from China and were thrilled to have the option of knowing their son's birth mom. Jenny and the family developed a relationship where she would come have a special day with the kids once a month. In addition to being birth mom to her son, she also took on the role of a "birth mom" to the adopted girl from China. After a while, the "infertile" couple gave birth to a third child, and Jenny continued her monthly adventures. In a twist of understanding, the third child, now a preschooler, said to his parents, "I want a birth mother too!"

We were buoyed and surprised by the many stories we heard in this process. And as we unfolded our plans to our friends, we learned that many people whom we had known for years were also adopted or have adopted siblings. The things you don't know until you're in the situation yourself…

In domestic adoption, one is likely to meet the birth mother while she is pregnant, with the possibility of being at the child's birth; and if not at the birth, to meet soon thereafter.

In our case, a birth mother chose us when she was eight months pregnant. She lives just two hours away, so we got together several times before the baby was born, and we were present at the birth.

But I'm putting the cart before the horse.

In order to adopt, a family has to do a lot of things, including a "home study." This involves doing a lot of values clarification, filling in a very long personal profile about one's childhood, values, theories, and hopes in childrearing. As my husband and I had to articulate what we saw as our partner's strengths and weaknesses, we realized we were having great conversations about this adventure that our friends who had given birth had never considered. For example, "How did your parents handle discipline when you were growing up?" and "What do you think are your partner's greatest strengths? What are his/her weaknesses in parenting?" These amazing questions should be asked of anyone who wants to become a parent! While it was sort of arduous, and we felt judged when we had to submit our tax returns, our expenses, our fingerprints and Department of Justice records, it seemed like a very good process to vet those who might not be able to parent well. Perhaps all those expecting should have some kind of self-reflection and social checkup!

One of the hardest parts of this process was not knowing when we would be matched with a baby. It's not like being pregnant. In fact, around the time we went into adoption circulation, my boss announced that she was pregnant. As the months went by, her belly was growing. Conversely, although I was "expecting," there was no growth to show for it.

One day I overheard her in the company kitchen sharing her plans with a colleague. She was saying that her mother-in-law was planning to come in for a few weeks around the time of the birth, and that she was navigating all the family schedules.

Though this was not directed toward me at all, I felt my interior tense up and tears well inside, as I knew I could not make these kinds of plans. While our families were incredibly excited and supportive, we had met people in this process who had been waiting over a year for a contact from a birth mother. I felt so unable to control any of this.

I called a cousin - a mother of two - who comforted me greatly by sharing her experience of birth. Yes, she knew the approximate dates of her children's births, but she didn't know their eye or hair color, she didn't know what they would like or dislike, she didn't know what kind of people they would be. Her description of the existential unknowns helped me to let go of my desire to be able to plan.

However, as the months went on and we had no contact, I began to feel despair. I had envisioned that we would be waiting a total of four to six months until our baby came. So when those time markers came and went, I started to feel out of control again, and very sad. The adoption agency had monthly meetings for families who were waiting or who had just adopted. I started attending. I read books about adoption and stories of mothering.

At one point, I realized I could channel my anxiety into preparing for the arrival of a baby, and we signed up for classes in feeding, diapering, and what to do when you brought a baby home. It was very helpful in using my energy to prepare rather than to fret.

And sure enough . . . when I look back on all the timing, I took those courses at about the time I might have taken "childbirth" classes, had I been pregnant.

Finally, when a connection with a birth mother worked out, I immediately told the relevant people at my workplace, especially as there was only one month until the due date. They were incredibly supportive of our adoption journey. Our baby was due right around the 4th of July. On the Thursday just after the holiday, my boss asked me to change my voicemail and to set up an auto reply on my email. I did so, with the plan that when I came back on Monday I could turn it all off. I left work and went to a meeting for a committee I was serving on, saying goodbye for a bit, as I was likely to have a baby before the next meeting. It was all a bit strange, though, because in the back of my mind I thought even if she did give birth, she might change her mind. Or we might change ours. Or he might be sick. Or… God forbid, not survive. So I had all that worry.

And though the baby was due, I wasn't banking on becoming a mom overnight. I went home, straight to bed.

Around 3 A.M., I woke up to use the bathroom. My husband, who I thought was asleep, called in to me, "Stop making such a racket in there!"

When I opened the door, I called back, "Honey, my water broke!" Then I got back in bed. He was too sleepy to appreciate my cheekiness.

At 5 A.M., our phone rang. Bob picked it up, hearing the birth mom's mother on the other end letting us know that she had been in the hospital for two hours and we should come on up.

We called a friend to come get our dog, gathered a few things together, and hopped into our car to drive the two hours up to Sacramento, where our baby's birth mother was in labor. When we arrived, she had been up all night and in labor for hours already. It was around 9 A.M. by the time we showed up. It was quite a scene, with four of her friends hanging out on the floor, her mom with us, and us in shock.

At one point when the doctor came in to check her, we left the room, waiting down the hall. A few minutes later, her best friend ran into the waiting room in tears, saying the doctor said there was something in the way and that she had to have a cesarean section. We returned to find the birth mother in tears, worried, feeling like a failure, as she wanted to give birth vaginally. The doctors and nurses shooed us all away, and took the birth mother and her mother into the operating room. We sat outside, not knowing what to do with ourselves.

And less than fifteen minutes later, "Grandma" texted a photo of a little alien creature covered in goo, crying out. We ran to the doors outside the delivery room as "Grandma" came out in scrubs holding the little bird of a baby. He was so light. So beautiful. Peaceful. "Grandma" took a photo of us with our miracle baby. One that captures the awe and the sweetness.

I could hardly believe it all.

Before the birth, we had agreed that we would all leave the hospital together. The social workers and adoption agency had organized everything really well, so they expected us there. Since the cesarean mom had to stay in the hospital for a few days, the nurses set up a bed for us in the same room. We all spent three days there, all of us in our beds, with the baby in a bassinet between us. I am not sure that any of us actually slept, it was just so awesome. The little guy was super loved from the moment he emerged. We just marveled at his little fingers and toes, at his squawks.

The nurses set us up with an SNS, a supplementary nursing system, which allowed me to "nurse" the baby, with formula dripping through a tiny tube taped to my nipple. There was a lot of support by the hospital lactation team to help me navigate this system and to maximize my bonding with this little guy. They even showed Bob how to attach the tube to his finger so he could also feed the baby.

It was all so sweet! And strange!

We had agreed with the birth mom that she would provide the first nursing to give the newborn colostrum, which we had all heard was a great nutritional benefit for the overall health of the child. So she was nursing, I was nursing, the hospital staff came to weigh and check for jaundice at all hours. Several relatives showed up. I think we ate. I know we went to Target to get toothbrushes, diapers, and baby formula. At least we already had a car seat!

When the birth mother chose us, she did so with 100 percent certainty that she was ready to give this baby to a family. And she wanted us to be that family. She chose us partially because after seeing our pictures in the "Dear Birth Mother" letter, she thought he would look like he fit in with us (which he does) and because she liked that we both work in art-related fields.

She was already eight months pregnant and shared her journey - which included denial, then hopes that she and her boyfriend would reunite, then thoughts that she might raise the child alone, and then the reality that she really was not ready to mother. Her best friend's brother had fathered a child who was adopted two years prior by a family who lived near us (and two hours away from them). They saw each other nearly every month, for holidays as well as casual brunch. We all had that model in our minds. I think once we established that we were a match, we liked each other so much that we thought we would stay in touch regularly. (My husband and I lovingly joked, actually, that we had adopted a newborn and a twenty-year-old.)

From the day we met our baby's birth mother, Amy - we were deeply grateful. She was only twenty, but was making an incredibly mature decision to give birth and to not raise that child. Having given up alcohol when pregnant, and having taken excellent care of herself - prenatal vitamins, no sushi, swimming regularly - she was planning to start college that fall, heading into the field of farming and science education. Her own mother had given birth to her at twenty and had a rocky life, it seems, with her husband leaving, drugs and alcohol, and six more children. Our baby's birth mom was determined not to have that life. She went so far as to say her birth mother should have given her up for adoption.

So we were pretty hopeful. And grateful. And in the tidal wave shock of being new parents and having this little creature depending on us for everything.

The hospital experience was sort of timeless and surreal. When the birth mom nursed right at the beginning, the baby learned to latch on pretty easily. Our child was getting breast milk and formula. The nurses were really supportive and taught us how and when to feed the little guy with the SNS. The birth mom nursed a little bit, but as her breasts filled, she pumped the milk out rather than have the baby at her breast each time. In retrospect, I wonder if this was for her own emotional protection.

For three days and nights, we all shared a tiny room and cared for the tiny boy. We had offered to take his birth mother home after the hospital stay. On the last night, she asked if she could talk to me privately (meaning without my husband around). Of course I agreed, with an edge of fear that she was, after all this, changing her mind. In tears she told me she did not want us to take her home; she wanted her friends to come get her. I was still shaking, but of course wanted what would feel best to her.

It was hard to say goodbye and to leave our little Amy. To be honest, though, I had so much on my plate that I didn't think a lot about how hard it must have been for her to leave. My mind was filled with thoughts about keeping the baby safe for his first car ride, what supplies we needed at home, who would be there, the dog, food for us, etc. I didn't think a lot about what those days were like for Amy.

The following week, Amy came to visit with a small entourage of close friends. And bags of frozen breast milk that she had pumped for the little guy. Eight days after giving birth, this young woman showed up in a leather miniskirt and heels almost as tall as I am. And she brought a cake box of teddy-bear-shaped cupcakes to celebrate.

For another few weeks, she continued to pump breast milk (with a pump loaned to her by the hospital). Her relative, who worked near us, delivered it once or twice. And then it petered out. I think it was too emotional for her to pump. I think she wanted to heal from the birth and get on with her life. We saw each other again about a month later, in mid-August, when she came down with some friends. And again in September she came with a few friends for a family dinner. In October, we met at a restaurant halfway between our homes. I could see such a mixture of love and caution in her eyes. It was clear that she was smitten with this sweet smiley baby, yet she also wanted to hold back.

After that meeting, Amy did not engage in much communication with us. It's been hard. We do know from her mother that she's having a hard time, and that she thinks about the baby every day. When she is ready, she wants to be back in his life.

Luckily, we have the adoption agency, their experience and wisdom, to lean on. They will offer counseling to our child (and to us if necessary, I think). They have reached out to Amy. And they have experienced all kinds of responses to adoption. This is not unusual. When she feels stable and like she has something to offer to this relationship, she will be back.

She gave us the greatest gift ever and we have no way to repay her selflessness. I wish for her health. Success. I wish I could help her. But for now, I wait and send hopeful prayers.

A mother asked me about how things get better after the whole newborn stage. I think I just really stayed in my heart and my truth. I just did what I had to do. It is hard to explain, and this is a good question because it addresses the core difference between adoption and natural birth, because with adoption you only have to deal with a newborn, not handle postpartum recovery. Being asked this question was a marker - an opportunity, invited or not, to share that my son was adopted.

The most impactful part of becoming a parent is the love that comes with the responsibility. Loving the little person. The overwhelming and amazing responsibility for feeding, clothing, burping, and cleaning. Sometimes at the expense of remembering to care for myself! It is so profound how this little person cannot take care of himself – everything depends on us adults. And now that he's already two years old, I don't relate to him as adopted – he's just our son, Max. In fact, that's really how I felt from the beginning.

Conclusion

The emergence of a new person into the world can be overwhelmingly joyful. At the same time, in the aftermath of birth, there is an upheaval and sometimes even intense distress.

One theme that runs strongly through all the stories in this book is that the postpartum period goes far more smoothly when the parents have a strong support system in place. If there is no close family or community assistance nearby, parents can turn to professionals such as a postpartum doula, night nurse, or lactation consultant. Every family has its own dynamics, and what works well for one may not be the ticket for the next, but planning to have support after birth can make all the difference in having an easier postpartum period. This, ultimately, is the goal: That the mother can recover physically and emotionally from birth, for the baby's feeding and physical care to be well established, and for the family to smoothly integrate the new baby (or babies).

This book provides insights on how to structure the postpartum period for maximum support. Whether women are pregnant, postpartum, or their last birth was many years ago, it can be validating to read how other women experienced the post-birth time period. In addition to reading about others' post-birth experiences, here are some practical ways to get support during the postpartum period:

- Meal trains for families with a newborn. You can easily create one via a website like www.takethemameal.com
- New mothers' support groups.

- Breastfeeding support groups, such as La Leche League or others.
- Postpartum doulas for night time and/or daytime. DONA (Doulas of North America) offers certification, as do other organizations.
- Night nurses, and/or daytime nurses.

And of course, writing out one's own story can be exceedingly helpful for new mothers. Any time after the first few weeks postpartum, and even up until years later, mothers can write out their own post-birth experiences, as the mothers did for the stories in this book. In doing so, mothers not only process their own experiences, but also help open a new era of communication about this distinguished time in the life of a family.

Your Post-Birth Story

I encourage you to write out your own post-birth story. As a guideline for getting started, I pass on the simple words of wisdom that my longtime-friend Abby Friedman wrote on the first page of a journal she gave me for my sixteenth birthday: *Just write!*

CPSIA information can be obtained
at www.ICGtesting.com
Printed in the USA
LVOW03s1706300418
575398LV00002B/403/P

9 780998 855103